Bonnie and Clyde: Resurrection Road

Saving democracy, one bank robbery at a time.

Book 1

Clark Hays

Kathleen McFall

PUMPJACK PRESS

First Printing 2017
First Edition
ISBN: 978-0-9974113-3-1
Library of Congress Control Number: 2017935342
Cover design by *the*BookDesigners

Pumpjack Press
Portland, Oregon
www.pumpjackpress.com

This is a work of fiction.

Also by Clark Hays and Kathleen McFall

The Cowboy and the Vampire Collection (four books)
A Very Unusual Romance
Blood and Whiskey
Rough Trails and Shallow Graves
The Last Sunset

Also by Clark Hays

Just West of Hell

"We must especially beware of that small group of selfish men who would clip the wings on the American eagle in order to feather their own nests."

Franklin D. Roosevelt

"They call them cold-blooded killers,
they say they are heartless and mean;
but I say this with pride, I once knew Clyde
when he was honest and upright and clean.
But the laws fooled around and taking him down
and locking him up in a cell,
'til he said to me, I'll never be free,
so I'll meet a few of them in hell."

Bonnie Parker

CHAPTER 1

Graves, guns, roses, and secrets

The wind, a constant in the Texas panhandle, blew dust and tumbleweeds across the gravel road as he drove toward the little church. He was late and almost hadn't come at all. It was a last-minute decision made on a painfully slow news day.

He saw them at the far side of the cemetery—a woman and two young men leaning on shovels. Everyone else was gone—or maybe no one attended, he thought.

He parked his Chrysler LeBaron at a respectful distance, shouldered the rusting door to force it open, stepped out, and crushed his cigarette into the dirt. He straightened his collar against the breeze—still chilly in early spring—and walked toward the fresh grave.

It was a lonely tableau. Three people next to a pecan tree in a deserted graveyard, ominous clouds building on the horizon. He tried to burn the image into his memory in case the story panned out.

He focused his attention on the old woman. Black stockings covered spindly legs sticking out from the bottom of a full-length mink coat long out of style. With a vintage felt hat fronted by a lace veil partially covering her eyes, she was overdressed, even by Texas standards.

Drawing closer, he saw the embers of an ancient fire flash to the surface when she turned to smile at him.

1

"You made it," she said. "I was starting to think maybe you wrote me off as some crazy old bat."

"I haven't made up my mind one way or the other just yet," he said.

She laughed, a hearty sound, and turned to the pair of gravediggers—placid, sinewy young men standing nearby, bored but respectful of the dead.

"You boys can go on now," she said. She pulled out two twenty-dollar bills from a beaded purse that matched her hat and handed one to each. "Leave the shovels. But come back in an hour to tidy up."

The men looked at each other, shrugged, pocketed the cash, and walked toward the small brick church without saying a word.

A large canvas duffel bag lay at her feet. It looked heavy, and since she was a tiny slip of a thing, he wondered how she would carry it back to the car.

"It's good to meet you, ma'am," he said. "I'm—"

"I know who you are," she said, a southern drawl dripping warmth from the edge of her words. "Royce Jenkins. You write some history articles for *The Dispatch*, along with obituaries, high school football scores, and occasionally recipes. You're not half-bad—for a newspaperman, I mean."

"Thanks," Royce said. "I think that's called damning with faint praise."

She laughed again. "I've had more than my share of run-ins with the press. But my husband, God rest his soul"—she looked toward the grave—"my husband thought pretty highly of you after that piece you did on Texas prisons. You got a lot of that right."

"Not many people remember that article, at least according to my editor," he said, tilting his head toward the grave. "So, that's your husband?"

"My one true love," she said. "We were together for more than fifty years. Sometimes you're lucky enough to find the person you're meant to be with right off."

"I'm sorry for your loss," he said. "Mind if I smoke?"

"Can't think of a better place to kill yourself than a graveyard."

"I don't mean to sound crass, but lots of people fall in love and stay together a long time, and then die," Royce said, pulling out a cigarette. "You said you had a big story for me."

He was having serious second thoughts about driving all the way out here.

"The biggest story you'll encounter in your life, but first I was hoping you could help me." She pulled one of the shovels out of the fresh dirt and handed it to him.

"You want me to help bury him?" Royce asked. "That's a little outside my job description, and anyway, why not just let those two strapping young men earn their pay?"

"Because I don't want them to steal the guns," she said. "They're old, but they still work. He cleaned them nearly every day."

"Guns?" Royce asked, bushy eyebrows inching up.

She bent down, unzipped the duffel bag, and pulled out two rifles, each almost as long as she was tall. She handled the heavy guys with an ease born of familiarity.

"Are those...?"

"Yep, BARs," she said. "Browning Automatic Rifles, chambered in 30.06. He loved them almost as much as he loved me." She tossed them into the grave, where they landed on top of the coffin with a clatter.

Royce stared at the antique guns in amazement. The wood of the butts and grips matched the heavy lacquer of the coffin.

"Of course, you can't write about the guns," she said. "Or tell anyone about this. I don't want anyone digging them up."

He turned to look more closely at her, a thousand questions forming, but they died in this throat when he saw she was now holding a pair of well-used Colt .45s with the same unsettling ease, one in each hand. She tossed them in after the rifles. "He wouldn't feel safe without his guns, even in heaven. At least I hope that's where he's going. Seems like we atoned enough for our sins."

The old woman bent over the duffel bag again, pushing the sleeves of the mink coat back to her elbows, and he half expected her to pull out grenades next, but instead she extracted a bouquet of red roses. Even behind the veil, he could see tears forming, but somehow it only made her seem fiercer. She tossed the flowers into the grave on top of the guns. "I love you, Clyde," she whispered.

He looked at the tombstone, confused. It read: *"Here rests Clarence Prentiss. May he finally find peace."*

"I love you more now than the day we met," she said, voice breaking. "And I don't regret a single goddamn thing. Not even from when we first started out." She glared at Royce. "Well, don't just stand there watching me bawl, start shoveling."

He flipped the cigarette and turned his attention to the grave, slinging in dirt. She took up the other shovel and followed suit, matching his pace until the guns and roses were gone from sight, hidden under the freshly turned earth.

When the grave was filled, he dropped the shovel and looked at the angry blisters rising up on his palms. "Who was your husband?" he asked, wiping the sweat beaded on his brow. "And what's with the guns?"

She was winded but hid it well with a stubborn jaw. "His name is—was—Clyde Barrow," she said.

"Same as the famous outlaw?" Royce asked. "That's funny."

"No, not the same as," she said. "The original. My name is Bonnie Parker. Although around here, they know us as Brenda and Clarence Prentiss."

"Bonnie and Clyde?" Royce said.

"In the flesh—at least what's left of it."

"Ma'am, no offense, but they both died in the 1930s, a long time ago."

"Fifty years ago exactly," she said. "He always knew how to make an entrance. And an exit, I guess."

"Wait, you're Bonnie and Clyde?"

"I told you it was a big story," Bonnie said. "Now that Clyde is dead, I plan to tell the truth. I never cared much about what happened to me, but there was no way he was going back to prison."

It was impossible, of course, but even a story about two old people pretending to be Bonnie and Clyde could be something worth hearing. Royce pulled out his notebook. "Tell me about the holdups."

"Slow down, champ," she said. "I have conditions."

"Conditions?"

"You can't publish anything until you hear the whole story, and that may take a while," she said. "After that, you're free to write anything you want, except about the guns buried here, of course."

"I can live with that," he said.

"And I want you to find out some things for me— things I need to know to go to my maker peacefully."

"Like what?" he asked, playing along.

"First off, I want to know how they faked our funeral.

The second thing I want to know is who was in that car that got shot up in 1934. Somebody died for us, and I need to know who it was. And the third thing I want to know is who we were working for these past fifty years."

"Wait, working for?" Royce said. "I don't know much about Bonnie and Clyde, except for that movie, but I always thought you were on your own."

She laughed. "That damn movie. Pretty flattering to be played by Faye Dunaway—such a beauty. Poor Blanche, though. She came off as a screechy imbecile. Estelle Parsons played her for a ninny."

"Ma'am, Bonnie or Brenda, I don't really have much time here today to talk about movies." Royce looked at his watch.

"Oh, I'm sorry," Bonnie said, her eyes going hard under the veil. "Am I boring you with the biggest story of your goddamn career? By all means, head on home and write up that article on the prize-winning steer that might get you a Pulitzer."

"Sorry," Royce said. "I'm just a little bit…" He struggled to find the words. "This is a lot to take in. Why don't you start at the beginning, and I can figure out what there is to tell?"

She relaxed and smiled. "Time is a funny thing," she said. "I've had a long time to think about the beginning of our story, me and Clyde. Truth be told, the real beginning was back before we even met, when a handsome, impulsive young man—just a boy, really—dared to want more than society said he was due. That was in West Dallas, a real hellhole. He was put in jail for something small and then terrible, terrible things happened to him there, and all that rage and anger spiraled out of control until someone focused it in a better way."

Royce scribbled a few lines in his notebook.

"But our story also starts when he met a stupid young girl who was lost and alone and desperate to feel different and special," she said.

"Sounds a little melodramatic," Royce said.

"Let's start someplace else then," she said, smiling. "Let's make Friday, May 25, 1934, the beginning of our story. Two days after the world thought we died and the day we got our first assignment."

CHAPTER 2

Reports of your death are greatly exaggerated

"Have you heard the news?" the woman asked. "The infamous Bonnie and Clyde are dead. Gunned down in an ambush. Cut to pieces by four Texas Rangers with Tommy guns."

She tossed a thick, folded newspaper—a copy of the *Dallas Morning News*—onto the plain metal table in front of two shackled prisoners, a man and a woman.

"Can you both read?" she asked. "Allow me: 'Posse kills Bonnie Parker and Clyde Barrow,'" she said, reading the headlines upside down. "'Elusive Dallas desperadoes shot to death in Louisiana.' The pictures really do you justice. You look—I don't know—taller," she said to Clyde. "And prettier," she said to Bonnie.

Clyde bristled and tugged at the handcuffs. His eyes were heavy, his thoughts slow to form. He looked over at Bonnie, and she shrugged helplessly. He'd never seen her look anything less than certain before, even when things were going to hell.

"With so many bullets, your bodies are barely recognizable," the woman said.

The photographs showed two bloodied corpses. A man and a woman. The bodies were spread carelessly across a greasy wooden floor. An army of excited gawkers looked through a storefront, palms pressed against the glass.

"They may be dead ringers for us, be we obviously

8

ain't dead," Clyde said.

"I am the only person in the world right now who knows that to be true," the woman said. "Take a moment and let the implications of that fact sink in."

"Is this some kind of joke? Like one of them gag papers or something?" Clyde asked, his voice rising.

"I assure you it's no joke," the woman said. "In fact, this may be the most important few minutes of your sorry lives. You get to decide whether you're really dead, like the papers say, or if you live."

"Why are we even talking?" Clyde asked. "We killed people. Cops and regular people. We're guilty as sin and you got us dead to rights."

Clyde tried to make out where they were. The room was nearly dark. There were no windows, so maybe it was night. It felt damp and smelled like old dirt, used-up engine oil, and onions—a cellar maybe.

"If we didn't think you were useful, we wouldn't be having this conversation," the woman said. "It would really be you in those photos, and I would be having coffee and toast at the New Penny diner on Dupont, planning my day."

"What do you mean, useful?" Bonnie asked, the fire returning to her eyes. The last thing she remembered was being pulled out of the car.

"Ah, so the notorious Bonnie Parker has a voice," the woman said. "I was starting to worry that maybe your vocal chords were broken."

"I wish my ears were broken so I didn't have to listen to you yammering on," Bonnie said.

The woman leaned forward and swept the newspapers off the table. "You were a useful lesson for those Texas rednecks passing themselves off as the law. We told them—we warned them—it's a simple equation: poverty plus brutality equals violence. We liked the lesson you were teaching them, and it got even better when people started to see you as symbols of the forgotten man."

She pulled up a splintered wooden chair and sat down facing them.

"You were a big slap in the face to the capitalists trying to take over the whole damn country and ruin it for everyone except them and their cronies. We always knew it was going to end in a violent death—yours, I mean— but until then, you provided a level of excitement that made the fat cats nervous. But when you started killing cops, the story got away from us."

"Who exactly is the 'we' in your story?" Bonnie asked, struggling to make sense of the rapid-fire words coming from this woman's mouth.

"That's not your concern. What is your concern is what we could possibly see in a couple of incorrigible lowlifes that would cause us to go to such great lengths to pluck you out of the very mouth of hell and put you in this room."

"That was gonna be my next question," Clyde said. "Maybe not in them exact words."

"You probably wouldn't have said 'incorrigible,' for one," Bonnie said, amplifying Clyde's bravado out of instinct. And habit.

"Turns out you're pretty good at staying alive and getting out of tight spots," she said. "Or maybe it's dumb luck. Guess we're about to find out. Your little crime spree ended two days ago. Now it's time to give back and help this country of ours stay on track."

"Fat chance, lady," Clyde said. "We ain't never gonna help the law."

"Oh, I think you will," she said, leaning back in the chair. "You're about to earn your lives back."

"Yeah, what makes you think that?" Bonnie asked, her head finally clearing.

The woman pulled a .38 from a shoulder holster. "If you refuse, I kill you both, right here, right now, and we dump your bodies in the Sabine River, no one the wiser. And then I have my people arrest every single person you know—your mothers, your sisters, your friends, the kids you sat next to in class, your teachers, even your god-damn pharmacist—anyone who ever shared a passing smile with the infamous Bonnie and Clyde—and we throw them in that hellhole prison you hate so much. Forever."

There was a long silence as Clyde looked at Bonnie.

"Can we talk about it a minute?" Bonnie asked. "Privately?"

"Oh sure, take all the time you…hell no, you can't talk about it. This isn't a Sadie Hawkins dance. I'm going to count to three, and if you say yes, we keep talking and figure out the details."

She looked at Bonnie. "If you say no, I put a bullet in handsome Clyde here, let you watch him die, and then I shoot you."

The woman walked around the table, pressed the barrel of the gun against Clyde's temple and cocked the hammer.

Bonnie stiffened, but her eyes shone defiantly, and she thrust out her chin. She looked at Clyde.

"I love you Clyde, more than life itself," she said softly. Then she turned her eyes back to the woman. "But dead or alive, nobody tells us what to do."

"Got it," the woman said. "You're the one with the balls. That makes so much sense." She moved and pressed the gun against Bonnie's cheek, hard enough to push her head back at an odd angle, like her thin neck might snap from the pressure.

"What do you say, Clyde? Ready to watch me splatter your pretty girlfriend's head all over the wall? One, two—"

"No, no," he shouted, straining against the cuffs and trying to stand. "Leave her be."

"Shut up, Clyde," Bonnie said, glaring at the woman.

"We'll do it, whatever it is," Clyde said. "We're in."

The woman nodded. "Good. I hate the smell of brains." She thumbed the hammer down, holstered the gun, and walked to the door. "Time to get you cleaned up. You both stink like week-old garbage left in the sun."

After she left the room, and the door closed behind her, she slumped and leaned against the wall, breathing out a long sigh of relief. She looked at her hand, trembling, and clenched her fist to stop the shakes.

"They're in," she said to a man standing on the other side of the dim hallway in the basement of the Grange hall in Carthage, Texas.

The man was big and solid, ill at ease in a new suit and holding a pump shotgun awkwardly with hands that made the weapon seem small and dainty.

He adjusted his fedora, tugging it into place. "I sure hope this is worth it."

"Me too, Carl," she said. "We've already paid a high price with what happened in the ambush."

"These two here seem like pretty bad people," Carl said.

She nodded. "We're counting on that."

CHAPTER 3

Introducing Mr. and Mrs. Prentiss

Bonnie leaned back in the tub of water, resting her head against the metal edge. Her ankle was shackled to the faucet. The halfhearted suds were flecked and mixed with the grime of weeks on the road, and the temperature—barely hot to begin with—had cooled to lukewarm.

She was puzzled that Clyde had given in so quickly. He should have called that woman's bluff. Those photos—they had to be faked somehow. But how or why? And where was Clyde now? She felt nervous being separated from him.

She touched her leg where the burns were beginning to heal. The skin looked like chewed bubble gum, faded and old. On the road, they'd been unable to get to a doctor for fear of being recognized. The soap and water stung the injured skin like turpentine.

"Time's up," the woman said, pushing aside the screen. Bonnie saw her grimace when she looked at the scars. "Those are hideous."

The woman pulled out her pistol. With her other hand, she bent down and unlocked the ankle cuff. It fell into the dirty water with a splash. She threw Bonnie a towel and stepped back. "Dry off."

"Where are we?" Bonnie asked, as she stepped out of the bath.

"None of your concern," the woman said.

Bonnie dried herself slowly, looking around for potential weapons or exits, showing no embarrassment at being naked. Some sort of basement room. No windows. A jumble of old furniture piled against a wall. In the far corner, bits of light slipped through spidery cracks in the concrete foundation.

The woman looked at Bonnie critically. Before the bath, she had cropped Bonnie's hair short and dyed it blonde.

"I don't think even your mother would recognize you," the woman said.

"That's a mean thing to say," Bonnie said. "What's your name, honey?"

The woman ignored her question. "The clothes on that chair are for you. Put them on—everything but the stockings. Don't try anything or I'll kill you. There's nowhere to run. The door's locked from the outside."

"I've got to call you something," Bonnie said, pulling on thick undergarments, a camisole, and then a plaid skirt.

"Call me Suicide Sal," the woman said with a tight smile.

"That's from my poem," Bonnie said. "How do you know about that?"

"We know everything about you. Now get the rest of your clothes on. I'm tired of looking at your bony ass."

"Plain clothes for a gangster moll," Bonnie said, buttoning the white blouse close up to her throat as she examined her reflection in the shattered and dusty mirror leaning against the wall. "I hardly even recognize myself," she said. She looked like a schoolgirl, young and innocent—only one who had seen and done a hundred terrible things.

"That's the point. By the way, your new name is Brenda Prentiss."

"That's real creative. Where's Clyde?"

"You mean Clarence Prentiss," she said. "He's going through his own transformation. Sit down in the chair and put your hands behind your back."

Bonnie did as she was told, still trying to plot how to get the gun out of Sal's hand and the door open. As if reading her thoughts, Sal cocked the hammer and leveled it at Bonnie's cheek while she snapped the handcuffs into place around her wrists. Then she holstered her gun and kneeled down in front of Bonnie, pushing her skirt up and her legs apart.

"What the hell do you think you're up to?" Bonnie said, and then forced a smile. "That isn't really my style, but I guess we could cut a deal."

Sal ignored her, and reached for a tube on the nearby table, squeezing a ribbon of oily paste into her palm. She lightly rubbed the ointment into the burns. It stung like mad, and Bonnie jerked back and cried out.

"Relax," Sal said. "This will speed the healing. It stings now, but that will pass. That car accident did a number on you. I thought your man was supposed to be a better driver than that."

Bonnie considered the woman kneeling in front of her. She wore a tan tweed suit with beige nylons. Her hair was cut in a style that went out of fashion years ago. No makeup. Her ring finger was bare. No surprise there, Bonnie thought.

Sal taped bandages into place over Bonnie's thigh and then stood back to admire her work.

"Thanks, Florence Nightingale," Bonnie said, the pain already subsiding.

Sal looked at her, wondering if she would regret the words about to come out of her mouth.

"You should probably be a lot more afraid about

what's happening to you. Why aren't you pitching a fit?"

"If you really knew everything about us, you'd know we tend not to overthink things," Bonnie said. "We just take all the shit life throws at us and throw some back when we can."

"Somehow I suspect that might be more Clyde's way of living than yours," Sal said. "That maybe you're going along with the lowest common denominator because it's easier."

"That's none of your business," Bonnie said.

"Everything is my business now, and don't try throwing any shit back at me," Sal said. "I own you both."

There was a knock on the door, and Sal rapped back. A bolt scraped across the wood frame, and the door opened. Carl, a good twelve inches taller and fifty pounds heavier than his prisoner, pushed Clyde forward into the room. Clyde was shackled at the wrists and ankles.

"Bonnie, you okay?" Clyde asked, shuffling forward.

"Yeah, baby," she said.

His black hair was cut short in a military style, buzzed close to his head, and he wore a new gray suit that fit him well. His shoes were polished to a dazzling gleam. She'd never seen him look so fine, and when he smiled wide, relieved to see her, she felt a little dizzy. Despite the crazy circumstances, a ball of electricity was creeping up and down the small of her back.

Clyde looked Bonnie over. "Lady, I don't know who you are, but you're damn near as good-looking as my number-one gal, Bonnie," he said.

"Do I really look all right, Clyde?" Bonnie asked. "My hair is so short."

"Bon, I look like a damn grunt someone melted and poured into a three-dollar suit."

"You look mighty fine," she said. "Like a leading man in the movies."

"Shut up, both of you," Sal said. She nodded at Carl. "Take them to the interrogation room. It's time they learned about their first assignment."

CHAPTER 4

A suicide mission

The newly minted Brenda and Clarence Prentiss—Bonnie and Clyde just minutes before—sat side-by-side in severely uncomfortable metal chairs, the ramrod straight backs forcing them to sit erect and at attention. Each had one wrist handcuffed to the heavy chair leg, and they were just far enough apart from each other to prevent contact.

The room was dark save for a single light bulb hanging down over the table by a cord. Sal nodded to Carl, and he walked outside and locked the door behind him.

Sal dropped a thick folder on the table for dramatic effect. "It's showtime," she said. She flipped it open and pulled out a black and white photo. It was a shot of Bonnie—a cigar between her teeth—leaning against the car with a pistol in her hand.

Clyde whistled. "I always loved that photo."

"I hate it," Bonnie said. "I look ridiculous, and it made half of America think I'm some sort of cigar-smoking, gun-toting she-devil."

Sal dropped more photos onto the table: Clyde sitting on the front bumper of a car holding a rifle; Clyde picking Bonnie up with one arm, a white fedora in his free hand; Bonnie aiming a gun at Clyde.

They exchanged a quick glance, remembering that day

and a rare moment of peace and happiness when they had some kicks goofing with the camera. All of that ended abruptly when the law caught up, and they bolted in a hail of gunfire, leaving the camera behind, loaded up with the exposed film. Within days, the photos were wired to newspapers around the nation, and the couple became instant celebrities.

"Call it what you want, but folks around this country sure thought they were seeing something special in those photos," Clyde said.

"What they thought they were seeing was two not horribly unattractive youngsters having illicit sex, robbing banks, and breaking all the rules," Sal said. "Every man wished he was Clyde, and every woman wanted to be Bonnie."

Sal tossed a copy of a newspaper clipping on top of the pictures. "And then it all went to hell because you started shooting cops and innocent people."

More clippings about the exploits of the outlaw couple followed—car chases, shootouts, murders. The stories chronicling their descent from folk heroes to cold-blooded killers soon blotted out all traces of the smiling photographs from happier days.

"That's the problem with public opinion," Sal said. "It's fickle. By the end, they were clamoring for your heads."

Clyde shifted uncomfortably in his seat, the unforgiving metal hard against his thighs. "I ain't lost a minute of sleep over what we done," he said. "You starve and kick a dog long enough, someday that dog's going to rise up and bite you."

"Or at least give you fleas," Sal said. She pulled up a chair to face them, a pistol on her lap.

"This moment is when you get one last chance to rise

above your past, rise above the killing, rise above your roots and your mistakes," she said. "Because when I look at all this murdering and thieving and daring escapes by the skin of your teeth, I see two people with the unique talents to do a job we need done."

"You want us to rob and kill for you?" Bonnie asked.

"We want you to save President Roosevelt from an assassin."

"What the hell are you on about?" Clyde said.

Bonnie held her tongue, waiting for what was coming next.

Before Sal could continue, there was a knock from outside. She opened the door and took a paper bag and drink carrier from Carl, and then he closed the door and locked the bolt back into place. They watched as Sal unpacked two turkey sandwiches wrapped in wax paper and three cups of coffee. She put a sandwich and coffee on the table in front of Bonnie and Clyde and then took a coffee for herself.

"Eat. You'll need your strength, and we have a lot to go over."

Clyde tore into his sandwich with his free hand and started wolfing it down, but Bonnie—even though she was ravenous—ignored the food and watched Sal coolly.

"May I have a smoke?" Bonnie asked.

Sal pulled a pack from the bag and tossed it on the table, waiting until Bonnie shook a cigarette free and then struck a match. Bonnie contemplated catching her by the wrist and holding her while Clyde took her pistol, and she felt Clyde tense in mid-bite, anticipating her play.

Sal waited until the cigarette caught and then leaned back. "Don't bother. He has orders to kill us all if need be," she said.

Bonnie inhaled deeply and then puffed out a thin

cloud of smoke.

"You think of almost everything, don't you, honey," Bonnie said, slowing down her words, stretching them out in a sugary drawl. "Except the right kind of cigarettes. I don't care much for menthols."

"I'll keep that in mind," Sal said, letting a sarcastic tone change the meaning of her words. She settled back into the chair and pulled back the lid on her coffee.

"What I'm about to tell you will undoubtedly be above your heads, but I'm going to explain anyway on the off chance some will sink in," Sal said.

Bonnie rolled her eyes and then tilted her head, puffing out a series of smoke rings that rippled toward the light bulb as if she was playing a game, trying to catch the light with a smoky lasso.

If Sal noticed her provocation, she didn't show it. "This country is at a delicate moment. Everyone's favorite democracy could still go down the toilet."

She placed a single picture on the table: a young, dark-skinned man with angry eyes and a face shaped like a dumdum bullet.

"Giuseppe Joey Zangara," Sal said. "He attempted to assassinate then president-elect Franklin Delano Roosevelt. He failed, but he managed to accidentally kill the Chicago mayor in the process."

"He's handsome enough, in a rugged sort of way," Bonnie said, tapping the ash from her cigarette onto the floor. "But certainly not his best angle." She took a sip of coffee.

"It's a pretty good angle for a photo when you think about it," Sal said. "It was the last time he was photographed alive. This was taken a few days before he was electrocuted. The trial was rushed, and he met his end on old Sparky before those who cared about the truth could talk to him."

"Could you get around to telling us how any of this applies to the fact you kidnapped us?" Bonnie asked.

Sal took a long sip of coffee, and then rubbed her temples with her thumbs.

"This country is still teetering on the brink of economic collapse," Sal said. "Farmers are going broke, people are starving. FDR pulled us up out of the ditch with the New Deal, but he's not done yet. Wall Street has to be reined in, and the rich need to pay their share to fix the damage they inflicted on the country, either directly or indirectly. But the president has to be alive to get it done."

Sal tossed a photo of three people onto the table: an older man with dark skin and long sideburns who could have been Zangara's stout uncle; a woman who looked to be in her late thirties with striking eyes and pearl earrings; and a younger man in a dapper suit with a bowtie and straw hat that did little to hide his oversized ears. All were standing on the steps of a marble-columned building.

"The man on the left is Percival Stubbs, majority owner of the First Independent Bank of New York. In the middle, Angela Dunthorpe, heiress to the Dunthorpe steel fortune. And on the right, Archibald Farquist, of the British Farquists."

"They made munitions during the Great War," Clyde said, wiping a trace of mustard from his mouth on the sleeve of his new suit.

"Very good," Sal said. "You have read something other than your own lurid crime stories. The Farquists made bombs for both sides, along with mustard gas and medical supplies. They made money no matter who was winning the war."

Clyde pointed at Bonnie's untouched sandwich, and

she pushed it over to him.

"What do these grinning idiots have to do with the dead Italian?" Bonnie said, deciding to follow Clyde's lead, pretending to be interested.

"We think these three hired Zangara to kill the president. And then used their wealth to rush the execution before Zangara could spill the beans. They want to stop FDR so they and their fat cat industrialist friends can keep on bleeding every last cent out of hard-working Americans."

"Those are some bitter words, honey," Bonnie said. "Did some rich sweetheart leave you at the altar?" She didn't give Sal time to answer. "And anyway, I read about Zangara in the papers. He hated capitalists. That Italian said he tried to kill the president to help poor people, not to help the rich."

"I'm going to let you in on a little secret," Sal said. "Not everything you read in the newspapers is true. For example, your life on the run seemed pretty exotic—fancy clothes and lavish parties. Was that really the case, or did you spend most nights shivering next to some shit-filled stream, wondering if you'd wake up with a bullet in your skull?"

"It ain't outlandish to think he really wanted to strike a blow for the working man," Clyde said. "Everything is stacked against poor folks. All the law does when poor people try to get by is round us up and throw us in jail and make us work there for free."

"Oh, poor Clyde," Sal said. "The law was so hard on you." She slammed her hand down on the table hard enough they both jumped. "For stealing chickens, cars, and money, in that order. Look, you both had it rough growing up, and prison didn't help, but don't try to duck your consequences. You killed people."

"Folks set your house on fire and then try to stop you from getting out, they're gonna get hurt," Clyde said.

"If we didn't think a rigged economic system had something to do with the stupid choices you both made, you would have died in that car instead of two unlucky patsies," Sal said.

"Pretty big risk for those three grubby cabbage farmers to step out of the shadows and do something so dangerous," Bonnie said, looking at the photo. "Must be a whole lot of money wrapped up in keeping things as they are."

"Or a lot of dough to be lost if the New Deal gets through," Clyde said. "What makes you think someone is getting ready to have another go at him?"

"We've got eyes in the right places," Sal said.

"How do they know one another?" Bonnie asked, pointing to the two men and woman in the photo.

"They live in New York and run in the same circles," Sal said.

"Do they work alone?" Bonnie asked.

"We don't know," Sal said.

Clyde finished the second sandwich and crumpled the wax paper. He threw it at a trashcan in the corner of the room and missed. "Nice story, lady, but we ain't no stool pigeons," he said. "That's the lowest kind of person."

"We don't need your singing voices," Sal said. "You're going to help us make sure the good guys win."

"That's rich. We're the bad guys, and it's not clear which side you're on, either, come to think of it," Bonnie said. "Who's to say you're not just working for some other rich folks, trying to do these ones in?"

"You don't need to know who we are. You just need to follow instructions," Sal said. "You behave and help save the president, you'll live and maybe have a pretty good life. You misbehave, your family goes to jail, and then we'll hunt you down and kill you. Or maybe just cripple you and put you in jail with your family so you can explain to them, over and over, why they're behind bars."

"Why don't we just kill them for you?" Bonnie asked. She shook out another cigarette and waited for Sal to light it. "We sink the good ship USS Greed, problem solved, and we disappear with our fancy new haircuts."

"If it were that simple, we wouldn't need you," Sal said. "They've hired another assassin. We don't know who it is. That's who you have to find before the president is brought down."

"So we just belong to you," Bonnie said. "No paycheck, no records. We're just supposed to trust you with our lives and the lives of our families?"

"I always suspected you were the smart one," Sal said. "Yes, you belong to us now, and we're holding your family hostage. Forever. From the moment we kept you from being cut to pieces in a hail of bullets, you became our property. Now pay attention. You know the targets. You've got ten days to get in thick with them and stop the assassin."

"How the hell are we supposed to do that?" Clyde asked.

"Use your imagination," Sal said. "And don't try to double-cross us. We'll be watching, and your families will pay the price."

CHAPTER 5

Sex with familiar strangers

After a grueling day learning more of the details of their assignment, night finally settled around them. Sal gave them each another sandwich—ham this time—and two warm orange sodas. Bonnie took a bite, spit it out and gave the rest to Clyde. When he was finished with both, Sal locked them in a tiny room with a bed and little else.

They were stretched out together on a sagging coil mattress on top of a squeaky bed frame, the restraints keeping them tantalizingly close but unable to embrace. Or run. Bonnie could hear mice scurrying between the walls.

Clyde tested the handcuffs that fixed his left wrist to the metal headboard, pulling until the skin around his wrist split and blood seeped into the starched cuffs of his new white shirt.

"Baby, take it easy," Bonnie said.

"You know I can't stand being locked up," he said.

She stretched out her arm as far as she could and stroked his cheek. She said the words she had been saying to him for the past year, each time he worked himself into this agitated state. "No matter what happens to us, what we got between us—this love, this fierce thing—it's always bigger than anything else."

He pulled on the restraint harder and shook his head

away from her hand, still struggling to free himself.

"Say it," she demanded, grabbing him by the chin. "Say we're always bigger than the worst thing life can throw at us."

"We're always bigger," he mumbled.

"You say it like you mean it, Clyde Barrow."

"Goddamn it, Bonnie, we're trussed up here like Christmas turkeys. I don't think a few words—"

She pinched him hard on his chest. "This is bad, but it ain't Eastham prison. Now say it like you mean it."

"All right, fine. You and me together are bigger than anything life throws at us."

"One more time," she said.

"We're bigger than anything life throws at us," he said, louder and with certainty.

In the darkness, she nodded. "That's right. And don't you forget it."

"I won't," he said. "But it don't make being made to dance like puppets on a string any easier."

"That won't last forever," she said. "Nothing lasts forever, except true love and Texas summers."

He laughed quietly, his face covered with shadows. Bonnie scooted a few inches closer to Clyde. She lowered her voice. "Breathe deep, baby, and tell me what you think is going on here."

"She's running some kind of con on us," he said.

"That's what I was thinking," she said. "Those photos, that newspaper—they're fake."

"There's no secret organization, no assassin," Clyde said. "It's just her and that mountain of a man and us in some shithole building they want us to think is a jail."

"It's odd, though," Bonnie said. "I can't figure out her angle. Why is she trying to sell us such a loony story?"

"If that dame is stupid enough to let us go tomorrow,

the last thing they'll see of us is our dust as we tear out of here. Just wait'll the whole world finds out Bonnie and Clyde are still alive," Clyde said.

"I don't know," she said. "If the world thinks we're dead, maybe we should stay in the grave. Mr. and Mrs. Prentiss could make a fresh start. Leave the past behind and start over. No running and no gunning. Just me and you doing whatever we want."

"That's something to consider," Clyde said.

"We just keep playing along for now?" she asked.

"Not like we have a lot of options," Clyde said, rattling his handcuff.

"We have one option," she said.

"What's that?"

"You look damn fine all cleaned up," Bonnie said. She reached out and pushed her hand down his pants.

"Bon, you little wildcat," he said, helping her unbuckle his belt and unbutton his fly, and then rolled over as close to her as he could.

"You look so goddamn handsome in these new clothes, with your hair cut short," Bonnie said. "All I could think about during them pictures she showed was how I wanted to do a little howling with you."

"I'm practically in bed with a new woman," Clyde said. "I can't think of the last time I was with a blonde," he said, pretending to ponder the notion. "Maybe it was back in Platte City."

"If you want to keep this thing attached to your body, I'd better be the last blonde you're ever with," she said, squeezing him hard.

Outside, Sal and Carl listened to the sounds from the bedroom through a hidden microphone—the moans and squeak of bedsprings and wet thumping.

Sal blushed, but just barely, and Carl looked at her

uncomfortably.

"I guess we know three things about them," Sal said. "They're still in love, they can't be trusted, and we have not yet convinced them we are serious."

CHAPTER 6

Skipping stones

The next morning, Sal and Carl barged in, roused Bonnie and Clyde from disheveled sleep, and escorted them back to the interrogation room one at a time, handcuffed and yawning.

"First things first, breakfast," Sal said. She placed two blue enameled plates loaded with scrambled eggs, biscuits, gravy, and grits in front of them, along with steaming cups of coffee.

This time Bonnie ate too, thinking it might be a while before they'd have another meal.

Sal dropped a leather wallet and a black, beaded purse on the table. "From here on out, you are Brenda and Clarence Prentiss. There's a driver's license for Clarence in the wallet and a birth certificate for each of you in Brenda's purse. There's also some money to get you started. This is important: don't use your real names. If you mess up and get caught, we don't know you."

After they finished eating, Sal nodded. Carl unlocked Clyde's cuffs and then freed Bonnie. Clyde bolted up from the chair and glared at the hulking man who dropped back and reached for the shotgun leaning against the wall. But Clyde just stood there, rubbing his wrist, making no move.

"It's okay, Carl. They work for us now," Sal said, with

more confidence than she felt, keeping a tight grip on the pistol hidden on her lap beneath the table. "Nothing to worry about."

Bonnie stood too. "We better get on the road if we hope to save the president," she said.

Sal nodded again and motioned at the door. They all walked out into the corridor and marched upstairs to the ground floor of the Carthage Grange hall. Outside, a new Buick Series 50 was parked in the shade of a graceful oak. Clyde whistled when Sal tossed him the keys.

"I am partial to Fords," he said. "But this'll do fine."

"There's a duffel bag of tricks in the trunk, and your guns are on the back seat," Sal said. "You'll understand if we ask you to drive on a ways before you pull out the shooting irons."

"I'd think less of you if you didn't," Clyde said. "Get in the car, Brenda, hon." Bonnie stifled a giggle.

"Time is not on your side," Sal said. "The faster you get to New York, the sooner we can disrupt the assassination plot."

Clyde slipped behind the wheel and clapped a new gray fedora on his head. "Don't you worry about a thing, Sal, or whatever your name really is—Brenda and Clarence are on the case."

Bonnie climbed into the passenger side and checked her lipstick in the mirror. "We'll send you a postcard," she said, turning to wave back at Sal and Carl, as Clyde roared the engine to life and tromped on the accelerator.

"How much money you think is back there?" Clyde asked, rolling down the window and breathing the free air deeply. Driving always calmed Clyde, making him feel like he was in control of the world—that nothing could keep them from living any dream.

"Hopefully just enough to get us someplace nice,"

Bonnie said. "You know, after we save the president."

He looked at her, and she arched her eyebrow, and they both started laughing.

Sal shielded her eyes and watched the car speed off into the distance.

"Think they're gonna bail?" Carl asked.

"Without question," Sal said. "Let's go. And bring your shotgun."

Once they felt comfortable with the distance between them and their former captors, and were convinced they weren't being followed, Clyde pulled off into a shady spot beside the Sabine River. The muddy water flowed slow and wide, and trash from earlier picnics littered the sandy banks.

Clyde pulled his .45s from the back seat, admiring how Sal and her team had cleaned and oiled them. He slipped the leather shoulder holster on and pulled his jacket closed, checking the reflection in the car window to make sure the gun bulge wasn't obvious. Bonnie was digging through the duffel bag in the trunk like a kid on Christmas morning.

"Grenades and dynamite and guns." She held up a little .25 auto, cycled a round into the chamber and dropped it into her purse. "We're set for war, if we wanted."

Clyde side-armed a flat rock into the water, skipping it halfway across, and then threw another. He was troubled, trying to figure out the con.

Bonnie opened an envelope filled with money. "Clyde, there must be like a thousand dollars in here," she said. "That's a lifetime of money."

"That's small potatoes," he said, skipping another flat rock. It bounced three times across the dark water then sank out of sight. "You deserve the moon, and I'm gonna get it for you."

"My dreamer," she said, continuing to rifle through the contents. "But why would she give us all this? I still can't figure out her game. Clyde, what do you think is going on?"

At the very bottom of the bag was the latest edition of the Dallas newspaper. She opened it below the fold, just as the sound of a car interrupted their idyll.

A police car.

Clyde stiffened and moved back toward her. "It's okay, baby. We're just a happy couple looking at the water."

The policeman, a fresh-faced young man, rolled down his window.

"Morning, folks. Everything okay here? Y'all having car trouble?"

"No, officer, we're just fine," Clyde said, smiling and waving. "Enjoying the morning."

"Ma'am, everything okay here? You look a little flustered."

Bonnie held up the newspaper. Plastered across the front page was the same photo of their bloodied corpses Sal had showed them the day before. "This picture rattled me a little," she said. "Such horrible people, but no one deserves this. Officer, I think this photo must be a fake."

"No, ma'am. I've seen the bodies myself, and if anyone deserves a horrible end, it's Bonnie and Clyde," he answered cheerfully from inside the police car. "Wished I could have put a couple bullets in their black hearts myself. I missed Barrow's funeral, but reckon I'll head up for hers after I get off shift."

Clyde watched as Bonnie looked down at the ground, hiding her shocked expression. He clenched his jaw and unbuttoned his jacket, set on wiping that stupid smile off the cop's face with bullets.

"That's a good idea," Bonnie said, recovering quickly, knowing she had to say something to keep Clyde from making a move they'd both regret. "Maybe we'll see you there."

The officer waved and pulled back out onto the road.

Clyde watched him until he was out of BAR range. "Asshole," he muttered.

Bonnie looked closer at the bloody photograph, and then held it up for Clyde to see. "How can this be true?"

Clyde had no answer. Bonnie leaned against the car, staring at the dead man and woman in the photo.

"Clyde, the paper says my funeral is this afternoon. We have to go."

CHAPTER 7

Back to the future

They sat in the front seat of Bonnie's red Cadillac de Ville out of the wind, watching the two young men pat down the gravesite with the backs of the shovels. The men kept shooting sideways glances at Bonnie's car as they made a production out of finishing the job.

"If they think I'm going to walk over there just so they can get another tip, they've got another think coming," Bonnie said.

Royce glanced at his watch. Shit. He missed the afternoon editorial meeting. There would be hell to pay for that.

"Okay to smoke in here?" he asked, mostly as an excuse to open the window.

She nodded, and he slid the window down an inch, drawing fresh Texas air into the stifling hot car. He could feel his shirt sticking to his sweat-soaked chest beneath his jacket as he lit a cigarette.

"Do you think you could turn down the heat a little?"

"Nope," she said. "When you're as old as I am, it's hard to stay warm, and that wind is cold."

Royce considered getting out of the car all together, but his reporter instincts beat out the discomfort of the heat and he decided to ask a few more questions. "How about you put me in touch with this Suicide Sal person?" he said. "That'd be a good first step at verifying what you're telling me."

The late afternoon sun had partially disappeared behind the towering clouds. Occasionally, a flash of lightning lit up the dark bands at the bottom.

Royce watched, as she seemed to struggle with his question. Her eyes narrowed, and a mudflat of crow's feet swept across her face.

"Sal isn't with us anymore," she said. "She was killed by the same bastards that put Clyde in a wheelchair."

Bonnie looked down at Royce's cigarette pack resting between them on the leather front seat.

"You want one?" he asked.

"I worked hard to give up them cancer-sticks," she said. "But what does it matter now?"

She reached for the pack and looked at the brand. "Menthols? What kind of man smokes peppermint sticks?"

Bonnie tossed the pack back on the seat between them and looked at the gravediggers. "Like they're building the Taj Mahal over there," she said. She honked impatiently and blinked the headlights twice.

They waved back in acknowledgment and worked faster.

"Kids," she said. "Look at them. You know, when I think about how young we were when all this happened. I was just a baby, twenty-four, and Clyde only a year older. How old are you, champ?"

"Older than twenty-four, that's certain," Royce said. "Never realized that Bonnie and Clyde were that young."

"We were young, and so in love, and so dumb," Bonnie said. "Didn't really think anything through. Just reacted all the time to whatever came our way, like bulls to a red flag."

She changed her mind about the cigarette, tapping one

out of the pack and holding it out for Royce's lighter. Bonnie smiled at the experience, like seeing an old friend, and blew out a single, wobbling smoke ring. Royce waited for her to continue.

"We learned a lot from Sal over the years. Learned how to channel our anger into something positive, how to push on the system in the hopes of making it work for everyone. She was a real patriot, loved this country. But in the end, I'm not sure the country loved her back," Bonnie said.

"What do you mean?"

"Fat cats are still getting fatter."

"What happened to her and Clyde, and when was that?" Royce asked, underlining in his notes what she just said about fat cats as a possible colorful quote for use in an article.

"All in good time," Bonnie responded. She rolled down the window and flicked the half-smoked cigarette outside. "Let's get this over with."

She killed the engine and stepped out, pulling the mink coat high around her neck. Royce got out as well, thankful for the cooler air.

Bonnie walked to the grave and made a show of inspecting how they had filled it in and piled the dirt up like a pitcher's mound.

"Good work, boys," she said, handing each another twenty-dollar bill. "And there's a lot more where that came from if you fine young men make it your business to keep this grave looking its best. I'll be out here every Monday, and if I like what I see, I'll have another twenty for each of you every week."

"Yes ma'am," the youngest one said, turning his red baseball cap around on his head so the brim pointed backward.

"You can bet we will be taking care of this here grave like no other," the older one said, pocketing the cash. "We'll keep the grass trimmed and the weeds pulled and make sure none of them pecan shells end up on it."

"Don't worry about that," she said. "He always did like pecans. But just so you know, if anyone messes around with this grave, I'll skin them alive," Bonnie said. "And you don't want to get on my bad side."

Both young men took a step back from her, shocked at the strong words coming from such a tiny old woman. "Don't you worry, ma'am, we'll be sure everything goes right," said the older one, haltingly, as they backed away.

Bonnie smiled and turned back to Royce. "You don't believe me now that there's no Sal to verify?"

"It's a pretty tall tale," he said. "It would help if there was someone else to back up what you're saying—a little proof."

"I admire your skepticism. It's the mark of a talented reporter. Maybe you think I'm lying."

"I'm not sure why you would do that, but it does seem like the simplest explanation for what's happening here. Simpler than believing you're Bonnie Parker," he said.

"It's getting chillier, and it'll be dark soon," she said. "Come sit in my car a little longer and I'll tell you about my funeral fifty years ago."

Her funeral? That would likely be a colorful tale, he thought. But then he felt bad, doubting this old lady on the day she had buried her husband. No reason not to humor her some more out of kindness and the off chance there was some story to be told. He had no pressing reason to get back to the newsroom at this late hour.

They walked back to her car in silence. "Feels weird talking about your funeral on the day of an actual funeral," he said. "You sure you're up for it?"

He opened the car door for her. Bonnie nodded and climbed behind the wheel. "Everybody secretly wishes they could go to their own funeral," she said. "Want to hear what folks have to say about them and see who shows up. But folks should be careful what they wish for. Because sometimes it comes true."

CHAPTER 8

Late to her own funeral

They pulled the Buick to a stop on a grassy knoll over-looking the Dallas funeral home. Bonnie looked down at the scene through a pair of binoculars included in the gear bag from Suicide Sal. Thousands of people thronged the small chapel. The streets were choked with cars, some barely moving, horns honking, engines revving at the gridlock, others parked haphazardly on lawns and in nearby driveways.

Flower bouquets and elaborate wreaths encircled the brick building like an army of colorful foot soldiers—mostly red roses and white lilies. On the edges of the parking lot, hawkers sold gunslinger memorabilia, lemonade, and fried chicken from crowded, makeshift stands. Children scampered around as if it was an unexpected holiday from school. Above, billowing gunmetal-gray clouds threatened a spring rainsquall.

"This can't be right," Bonnie said. "Why would all these people come to my funeral?"

Clyde checked the newspaper. "This is the right place."

"Are these people here because they love me or hate me?" Bonnie asked.

"Maybe when you're famous, it don't make much difference," he said. "Wait, something's happening."

She refocused the binoculars as a black sedan stopped

in front of the chapel, and her mother stepped out. She was tall and thin—frail even—wearing a black dress, and a matching hat with a veil. Even from that far away, Bonnie could tell she was tired and sad and drawn out.

Bonnie watched her mother take a few faltering steps toward the building and then stumble. Bonnie gasped and reached out to help her instinctively, as a cousin and a neighbor ran to her side. Holding her by the waist and elbows, they pushed past the gawkers and souvenir hunters, clearing a path through the crowd toward the chapel.

"What is it?" Clyde asked.

Bonnie handed him the binoculars. "It's my momma," she whispered. "I think I've broken her heart clean in two."

Clyde watched through the binoculars until Bonnie's mother entered the building, and then noticed more commotion.

"What in the hell?" he asked as a police car, lights flashing and sirens whining, slid through the crowd and stopped at the walkway. An officer opened the door and helped a woman, in handcuffs, struggle out onto the sidewalk.

"It's Billie," he said. "She's shackled."

"They already have my sister?" Bonnie whispered.

Clyde turned to Bonnie and tried to say something comforting but could form no words.

"This is impossible, Clyde. How is this possible?"

They sat in silence for a moment, gazing down at the spectacle.

"I've got to get inside," Bonnie said finally. "I've got to tell them this is all a lie."

Clyde grabbed her by the elbow. "I can't believe it, either, but what happens after you do that? The road is the only place we're safe. We'll figure out the con later."

"No," she shouted, twisting out of his grasp and climbing out of the car. "I'm tired of running. The only place it ever got us was farther from where we wanted."

"Bonnie, think this through," he said. "What kind of group could pull off something like this? Sal and her boys have got to be real dangerous."

"I don't care," she said, slipping on a pair of dark, oversized sunglasses. "I have to see this with my own eyes."

"Bonnie, I'm telling you, I'm ordering you, don't go down there," he said.

"I'll be back here directly," she said, pulling on a blue headscarf. "Wait for me. I won't do anything that skins us."

"Bonnie," he yelled to her retreating back, and she heard the temper building in his voice. But she knew he wouldn't follow her; he was, when all was said and done, a practical man. His limp on this downhill slope would make him too conspicuous.

Clyde watched her through the binoculars, boiling at her impulsiveness, but tempered with concern for what was about to happen, praying she wouldn't get hurt. He watched until she reached the chapel and then pulled out one of the BARs from the back seat. If things went to hell, at the very least he was going to send Sal, or whoever was behind this con, right into the lake of fire with him and Bonnie.

Bonnie reached the chapel as lines of people filed through the building to view the open casket. A gleaming black hearse idled by the curb, waiting to receive the body. Moving against the crowd, Bonnie found a side door. She gave a short wave up to Clyde, who she knew would be watching her closely, and disappeared inside.

The door led to the front of the chapel, and Bonnie slipped behind the crowd of people unnoticed, keeping the dark glasses on, feeling anonymous with short, blonde hair and respectable clothes.

She edged her way around the crowd. She had to see the body. A sightline cleared and Bonnie's breath stopped at the sight of a corpse that could easily be her twin, decked out in her favorite blue silk chemise, hair glossy and smooth, lips painted ruby red, resting on satin pillows. But even the thick pancake makeup that Bonnie could make out from twenty feet away could not hide the swollen and puffy face, disjointed from bullet trauma.

She edged closer, but a man in the vestments of a preacher, tall and thin with round spectacles, caught her by the arm. "Please, not so close," he said. "Show some respect for the dead."

Bonnie nodded and walked to the side of the chapel. She saw her momma sitting in the front row. Her back was rigid, her eyes downcast, as if bearing the scorn and derision of everyone who was there to revel in the downfall of a killer, while also bearing the dashed hopes of those there to mourn what Bonnie and Clyde once stood for—freedom.

Bonnie drew in a breath, ready to yell her mother's name, to tell her the truth, to beg for forgiveness, to bring it all crashing down, when a woman stepped in front of her, blocking—momentarily—the view of her mother.

"You related to that cop-killing bitch?" the young woman asked. She was pretty and pale, in a black dress trimmed in dark green lace. She held the hand of a plump little boy dressed in a gray suit. He had a police hat on that was way too big, slumping down and covering his eyes. Tear tracks cleaned through his fat, dirty cheeks.

"No, not related," Bonnie said, nervously. "Just a

friend of the family." She pulled the headscarf tightly around her face and tried to get away but the woman kept talking.

"Maybe you can tell them something for me," the woman said.

"Sure," Bonnie said.

"Tell them I'm glad she's dead. I'm glad her boyfriend is dead, and I hope they burn in hell. She killed my husband, this boy's father, just because he was wearing a badge. He was a good man, and we loved him. Now, we got no one to support us, and I don't know what to do."

The woman's eyes filled with tears. Bonnie handed her a handkerchief, and she used it to dab her eyes and nose, then offered it back. "No, please, keep it," Bonnie said.

"Can you tell them that for me?" she asked.

Bonnie nodded. "I'm sure she didn't mean it personal."

"Don't matter what she meant," the woman said. "My life is ruined." She picked up the boy and nestled her face into his shoulder. "Our lives are ruined," she repeated in a whisper.

"Don't cry, Mommy," the boy said, pushing the oversize hat back to reveal sky-blue eyes.

Bonnie remembered those eyes, the adult version, and the life going out of them.

The woman muffled a sob and turned away. Bonnie watched her walk back through the crowd and outside, uncertain what to do next, her mind shocked into submission, her body frozen.

Her mother stood near the coffin now, the preacher holding her arms and keeping her upright. She pulled a sheet of paper from a beaded purse, and it fluttered in her hands. "As the flowers are all made sweeter by the sunshine and the dew, so this old world is made brighter by the lives of folks like you," she read, and then she placed the paper inside the casket.

The attendants closed the lid, signaling that the service was about to begin. This had to end, Bonnie thought. She took a step forward just as someone grabbed her by the elbow.

"Hello, Brenda," Suicide Sal said, her face pressed close to Bonnie. "Fancy meeting you here." Her breath smelled of lemonade and tooth decay. "Watch what happens next."

A bulky man in a tight suit, out of place among the farmers and West Dallas rabble, walked up to Bonnie's mother and nodded close to her head, whispering. He opened his jacket, showing a badge and gun.

"What is he doing?" Bonnie asked.

"He's taking her to jail, of course. That was the deal, remember? Tough beans for her. I don't think she'll last long."

Bonnie's mother, confused, walked to the side of the funeral home with the man. At that instant, Bonnie's sister fainted and was carried out of the chapel by a policeman. "There goes another one. Still want to shout it from the mountaintop that Bonnie and Clyde never died?"

Bonnie jerked her arm free, turned abruptly and left the building, walking as fast as she could back to the car, pushing through the crowds, stumbling twice as she hurried up the hill, wincing in pain as the bandage fell off her burned leg. Her heart sank when she saw Clyde handcuffed to the steering wheel.

"I told you not to go down there," he said.

Bonnie leaned over and vomited against the whitewall tire. She spit the rancid taste out of her mouth and dabbed her lips with a spare handkerchief before rushing at Sal. "You let her go, you let my momma go," she screamed, lunging at Sal's waist.

Sal had her hand in her pocket, and as Bonnie got close, she pulled it out and—wearing a pair of brass knuckles—slammed her fist into Bonnie's stomach, knocking the air out of her. Bonnie fell to the ground, and Clyde cursed in anger. Bonnie threw up again.

Sal leaned in close to her. "We assumed you might need proof of just how serious we are," she said, her voice cracking. "We know you're not stupid. But this is it, your last chance. We've got eyes everywhere, and your mother stays in prison until you prove you can be trusted."

"Cover her," she said to Carl, and he pulled a .45 and aimed it at Bonnie. Sal unlocked Clyde's cuffs, and then without another word, she and Carl walked down the hill and disappeared into the crowd.

CHAPTER 9

Interview with a ghost

Royce followed Bonnie slowly up a rutted gravel road out of the graveyard, past the reservoir, and onto a county highway. The sun had almost set now, stretching long shadows of fence posts and mesquite trees across the road.

As he drove, he thought about the impossible story the old woman was spinning. But she had offered proof if he came back to her house. He had nothing to lose except a few hours on an already wasted evening.

Miles later, she turned onto a long driveway. At the crest, she parked in front of a modest clapboard house with a coat of faded yellow paint, surrounded by a scattering of outbuildings in various stages of disrepair and a large, multi-car garage, all of it on a hilltop that raised it higher than the surrounding prairie. It was lonely and isolated, with no neighbors in sight.

Like an Andrew Wyeth painting, thought Royce, as he stepped out of his car and looked across the desolate landscape. He was familiar enough with this part of the county to know this was an awful lot of agricultural land to keep out of rotation. Maybe it was leased to an oil company, but there weren't any pumpjacks in sight.

"Clyde bought up a pretty good parcel of land so we could have our privacy," she said, as if reading his thoughts. "And up on a hill, so we could keep a watchful eye on things."

She motioned for him to keep up. At the screened-in front porch, she took the steps instead of the wheelchair ramp and looked back at Royce from the top. "Even when we were old and washed up and needed help just getting up and down the stairs, he never quit thinking we might have to run at any minute," she said.

The house smelled of lemon furniture wax and gun oil. The pine floors were polished to a shine but the plain white walls were mostly bare—no photos, no artwork, nothing. It looked like a prison or a convent, he thought, or like a home that would be easy to leave in a heartbeat.

"Have a seat," she said, gesturing at an upholstered chair—a gaudy flower print—in the drab undecorated parlor. He sat back into the low, dainty chair, crossing and uncrossing his feet, trying to get comfortable, and looked around as she clattered in the kitchen.

She walked back in carrying a tray with an old-fashioned cut-glass decanter, an ice caddy, and two tumblers. He arched his eyebrow as she set it down on the glass coffee table between their chairs.

"I expected maybe some chamomile tea," he said.

"Why does everyone think old women like tea?"

Royce considered this, feeling momentarily chagrined. "Because you're always cold?"

She laughed. "You pay attention. I can bring you tea if you like."

"I do have to drive," he said. "But I can handle a short one."

She nodded and placed three ice cubes into each of the two tumblers and filled them to the rim with whiskey. Handing him the glass, she raised hers. "To Clyde," she said. "He had a good life, an interesting life, but he sure didn't get the death he wanted."

Royce raised his glass and then took a sip. "What kind of death did he want?" he asked, watching her face.

"To go out in a blaze of guns and glory, or in a fiery car crash—almost anything other than withering away in a wheelchair with ass cancer."

"Your husband, the man you call Clyde Barrow, was in a wheelchair?"

She nodded. "Yep. Took a bullet in the back saving me. Lost the use of his legs. Never begrudged me for a second, but he was always such an active man, so comfortable in his body, so it was pretty hard."

"I'm sorry," Royce said.

Bonnie looked down at her lap, the glass cradled in both withered old hands. She nervously scraped at faint remnants of dirt stuck behind her tiny childlike fingernails. Fearing she was crying, and completely unequipped to help her emotionally, Royce quietly took another sip of whiskey and contemplated making an exit.

After an awkward minute, she shook her head free of the memories and drained the tumbler in one long, uninterrupted gulp. "This should keep things interesting," she said, immediately filling her glass again. "You've heard that old saying, 'if you want the truth, bring the whiskey.' I know you think I'm crazy, so go on, ask me anything."

Royce put the glass on the coffee table and pulled out his notebook. "Well, ma'am, okay, and no disrespect, but the most obvious question first. How did they get you?"

"Get us?" she asked.

"Yeah, how did they pull you out of the car before the bullets started flying?"

"Clyde and I were in Louisiana. We'd been camping by Black Lake, and we had plans to head up to Sailes, but that night while we were sleeping in the back seat of the car, bandits raided our camp."

"Bandits?" Royce asked.

"You're familiar with the word bandit, aren't you?" Bonnie asked. "People with bandanas hiding their faces."

"Yeah, sure, bandits," he said. "It's just more of something you'd hear about with Pancho Villa down south of the border."

"All I know is they weren't cops or lawmen—leastwise they weren't wearing uniforms," Bonnie said. "They swooped in during the blackest part of the night and never said so much as 'boo.' They pressed rags across our mouths, and the next thing we knew, we woke up shackled in some dusty basement in a Grange hall in Carthage, Texas, reading about our own deaths in the newspaper."

"A Grange hall?" Royce asked.

"Sal had some sort of special connection with the Grange."

"Do you reckon they used chloroform?" Royce asked.

"Chloroform or fairy dust, it doesn't affect the rest of the story." The whiskey was loosening her up, the liquor adding a flush to her cheeks. "Next question?"

Royce scribbled in his notebook and then looked up. "How could a thousand people, and your own mother, not have known it wasn't you in the casket?"

"Tens of thousands," Bonnie said, a hint of pride in her voice. "And I don't know. It looked like me even to me. It was like looking in a mirror, only in the mirror I was dead and gone and perforated. I would have fallen to my knees if that preacher hadn't guided me to the wall."

He picked up his glass and drained it, rattling the ice cubes out of habit. She tilted the decanter to refill it, and he didn't stop her.

"All I know is that it sure looked like Bonnie Parker in that coffin, but it couldn't have been because Bonnie Parker is sitting right in front of you. Maybe you could get someone to exhume the bodies?"

"That would take a court order, an accommodating judge, and a pile of hard evidence," Royce said.

"None of which we have yet," she said. It was getting cooler, the front door was partially open, and she pulled a lap quilt over her legs. "Next question."

"How did you keep something like this secret for so long?" he asked.

"That turned out to be easier than either we expected. Once the news died down, and nobody was looking for us anymore, there was no reason for anyone to recognize us," Bonnie said. "There were a few close calls, but it was easy to laugh when anyone said I looked like Bonnie, and say something like, 'Oh, I get that all the time.'"

Royce finished the second glass and then pushed it out of her reach. His head was getting a little fuzzy, and a whiskey sweat had crept up the back of his neck.

"Who died in the car?"

"Don't know," she said. "But it bothered us both for all these years. Those Texas Rangers killed two people, thinking they were Bonnie and Clyde. I want to know who died for us."

He nodded and closed his notebook. "Ma'am, Brenda, Bonnie—whatever your real name is—I appreciate all the time you've taken with me, and the whiskey, but I came to your house because you said you had proof, some kind of evidence to back up your story."

She nodded and struggled up out of the chair. "Follow me."

She led him through the pristine kitchen and into the pantry. Pushing aside some empty decoy boxes, Bonnie pulled on a trapdoor handle. "Be careful on these steps," she said.

When she turned on the light at the bottom, he saw a different house, filled with personality, not the convent rooms upstairs. A worn sofa with a television in front of it. A few fake ferns. Lava lamps. A pair of antique ashtrays from the Hermitage Hotel in Nashville. An old radio. Framed photos all over the walls. A hospital-style sickbed, now stripped clean of sheets with a bare, tilted-up mattress. A wheelchair ramp up to a storm cellar door, locked from the inside.

She sat on the bed. "Go on, have a look at the photos."

He walked around the room. Some of the photos were the iconic ones he recognized from Bonnie and Clyde's youth, like her in a beret with a gun, smoking a cigar, and the rest were of her through the years, smiling as she moved from young woman, to middle-aged, to old.

"Where's your husband in all these?" Royce asked, thinking about the dead man in the cemetery buried beneath an arsenal.

"He never would let himself be photographed. Old habits die hard, and old crooks die harder. Took plenty of me, though," she said. She pointed at one half-hidden behind a lampshade. "But he's in that one."

Royce moved closer and whistled. It was Bonnie and her husband, glaring from his wheelchair, next to J. Edgar Hoover.

"You like that one?" she asked.

"Sure, but it could be a tourist shot. No proof there."

"Take a closer look, Mr. Newspaperman," she said.

He looked at the details and realized the photo had been taken inside the parlor upstairs.

"I thought you didn't know who you worked for?"

"We didn't. Neither did Edgar. Long after we hung up

our guns, he came to ask."

"And speaking of guns." She opened the closet door to the right of the Hoover photo. Inside was a battery of guns the likes of which he'd never seen—Tommy guns and BARs and shotguns. She smiled at his shock. "It gets better." She spun the dial of a wall safe and opened it so he could look inside. Money was stacked in tall piles, row after row—millions of dollars.

"Anything we took from the bad guys, Sal let us keep," she said.

She closed the safe and then pointed at some paintings wrapped in brown paper and leaned against the wall. "I got some pretty pricy artwork too," she said. "He collected cars and guns; I collected paintings. We needed something to do with all the money." She paused before adding, "And now I need someone to give it to when I die.

"No children?"

"Children? In this crazy life?"

"This is persuasive circumstantial evidence, but only circumstantial," Royce said.

"Do you want the story or not?" she asked. "Because I can take it somewhere else. They may not tell it as well as you, but it won't cost me near as much whiskey."

Royce thought. He looked around the room and rubbed his forehead, wondering if this was the craziest story he had ever encountered. He thought about the string of future articles on the Lubbock School Board, the cattle auction, and the high school football team waiting for him. What the hell. What did he have to lose but time. "Yeah, I want it," he said. "I want it."

She smiled. "Good. You're starting to grow on me."

"So what happened next?" he asked.

"Next we went to New York," she said. "But not before we blew some of Sal's money along the way."

CHAPTER 10

Gravel crossroads

Clyde drove like a madman to get out of Dallas, cursing and honking, weaving through the congested funeral traffic with his foot heavy on the accelerator. He didn't let up until they pulled onto Route 67.

Bonnie was silent the entire time, staring out the window.

With the city finally behind them, Clyde slowed down. They followed the same dusty back roads they had terrorized through years of evading the police, passing dozens of small farms boarded up and foreclosed. He finally turned onto a county dirt road that cut between anemic cotton fields and slid to an abrupt stop in a cloud of dust.

"You've got to talk to me, Bonnie," he said. "We need to figure out where we're going, what we're doing. Sulking ain't gonna help."

"I'm not sulking," she said, her voice dull and distant, like an ill-tuned piano. She rolled down the window, letting in cool air. The warm dusty wind disturbed flyaway strands of her hair, blowing a fine grit that stuck to her tears like sandpaper.

"I just can't believe all the people who came out to see me," she said. "Why would they do that?"

"It wasn't you," Clyde said. "You got to remember that."

"None of those people know that. My momma doesn't know that," she said. She turned to look at him, her face twisted in a mixture of anger, sadness, and uncertainty. "My sister didn't know that, and now they're both in jail."

He took her hand. "We can figure this out, Bon. We can handle whatever life throws at us. Ain't that what you always tell me?"

She shook her head, pulled her hand away and looked back out the window. "You told me prison is the worst place in the world. My momma can't live through that."

"What the hell are we going to do?" he asked. She heard an unfamiliar echo of desperation behind his words. Bonnie sat thinking, and Clyde waited, drumming his fingers on the steering wheel.

"We're going to head east," she said, flatly. "We're going to do their bidding. We're going to do what Sal told us to do."

"I ain't working for cops," Clyde said. "That's not a good plan, Bonnie."

"For one thing, we don't know if they are cops," she said. "And for another, it's the best play, so that's what we have to do."

"I got a better plan," he said. "We'll stop at my cousin's outside of Kansas City and lay low until we can get the Barrow gang together again and then go on the run. Canada or Mexico. And damn Sal if she tries to stop us."

Bonnie looked at him without saying anything. They stayed like that for a full minute, neither willing to break the silence, knowing whatever they said next could change everything between them. Finally Bonnie sat up straight in the seat, squared her shoulders, and spoke.

"You can be a nickel-and-dime crook until they shoot

you down for real," she said. "But I'm going to take this chance, for us and for our kinfolk. I don't blame you if you want out, but this is where it happens. One way of the other, with or without you, I'm heading to New York."

"I don't like the way you're talking to me, Bonnie," Clyde said, his voice rising. "Are you saying you're gonna leave me?" When she didn't answer, he jerked the door open and jumped out. He punched his fist into the hood, kicked the fender once, then again, savagely.

Bonnie stayed inside the car, counting to keep herself calm and to time out his temper. At a hundred, she reached into the back seat, pulled out the wad of cash and split it down the middle. She got out of the car, walked up to Clyde and pressed half into his hand. "Take your cut," she said.

"I don't want it," he said, pushing it away. "It's tainted money."

"It's all tainted. It's always tainted. That's what money is, Clyde," she yelled. Bonnie opened his jacket and shoved his half of the cash into the inside vest pocket. "Can't you see this is more than you or I have had our whole lives? Likely more than we'll ever have again. Who cares what we have to do for it?"

"Is this about getting rich or keeping our family out of prison?" Clyde asked.

"Can't it be both?"

The sound of an approaching engine cut through the emotions of the moment, and they looked down the dirt road. An old truck crawled toward them, loaded up with a mattress, suitcases, baskets, pots and pans—what looked to Bonnie like a family's entire belongings. Bonnie saw the vacant, hungry gazes of the children tucked almost out of sight against the cab and under the furniture.

"You all right?" the woman in the front seat called as they slowed down to pass. She'd seen enough of poverty and its toll to wonder if this slip of a blonde was getting a beating by the side of the road.

At his wife's urging, the man pulled over and got out of the car. He was in tattered overalls and boots without laces. The woman got out too; she was pregnant, her feet bare except for bundled up newspapers with twine making do as sandals. The kids didn't move from the back, just stared blankly.

"We're okay," Clyde said. "You can keep moving."

"If it's all the same, it feels good to move my legs," the woman said, throwing a look that Bonnie correctly read as a silent question of "Did she need help?"

"Really, I'm okay," Bonnie said. "Sweet of you to stop, though. Where you folks headed?"

"California," the man said. He was not impressed by the scene: a new car, fancy clothes, a pretty little woman not minding her own business, a hard man with a bleeding hand. The last thing he wanted was to get in the middle of something. "Reckon we'll be on our way, unless you be needing something. Come on, Mabel."

Bonnie pulled two twenty-dollar bills from her packet and pushed the cash into the woman's farm-rough hands.

"Take this," she said. "Take it and get to California safe."

"What are you doing?" the woman asked.

"Consider it a thank you for stopping to check on me," Bonnie whispered.

"We can't take your money," the man said, spotting the guns in the back seat through the open door. "Give it back, Mabel."

"I won't," she said. "God put these people on our path, and we will honor the kindness they showed us."

"Always listen to your lady," Clyde said to the husband, with narrowed eyes and an expressionless face that the man took as the threat Clyde intended. "They tend to get their way in the end."

"Damn right we do," Bonnie said, breaking into a smile that Clyde took in hopefully. "Hey listen, we have some food too. Let me get it for you. Have a picnic. It's a long road to California." She rummaged through the provisions Sal left in the car and pulled out three sandwiches, a jar of iced tea, and a pecan pie with one slice missing. She stuffed it all into a bag and handed it to the mother.

"We sure appreciate your generosity," the mother said.

"You'd really best be on your way now," Clyde said, pulling back his jacket so his shoulder holster was visible.

"Yep," the man said. "Let's get going, Mabel."

They watched the truck lumbering away, the dirty faces of the silent, uncertain children watching them the whole way.

Clyde looked at Bonnie. Even a hint of the possibility they might not stay together had made his stomach churn. "You know I ain't never gonna leave you," he said.

"I know," she said, catching him by the hand and pulling him close. "I'm not leaving you, either. We're in this together, until the bitter end. You can be awfully hardheaded sometimes, though."

"That's like getting advice on being less stubborn from a Georgia mule," he said. "You know if we do this—if we even make it out in one piece—you're gonna have to put your momma and your family out of your mind. Can you do that?"

Bonnie nodded. "I'll do what I have to, long as I know they're safe. What about your family?"

She kissed his skinned knuckles and then pressed his

hand against her breast.

"You're my only family now," he said, reaching into the car and dragging out a blanket. He spread it on the ground and pulled her softly down beside him. "And I hate it when we fight."

"What if some old farmer drives by?" she asked, the words ragged and caught between pleasure and concern as he pushed up her dress and she guided his hand between her legs.

"We'll just throw some money and sandwiches at him too," Clyde said, stroking her softly as she undid his belt.

"We really should get on the road," she said, biting her bottom lip as he thrust himself deep inside her.

"How about I do this real slow right now, and then drive real fast later?" He slipped out and then pushed himself in again to emphasize the point, and she trembled and clutched at his neck.

"Don't ever stop loving me like this," she whispered into his ear. "We can save America tomorrow."

CHAPTER 11

So this is room service

They drove through most of the night, stopping late at the Arkansas border for a few hours of sleep in the back seat. They woke up before the sun, stiff and chilled, and set their sights on making Nashville by sunset.

Being in a car together brought them as much joy as almost anything, and with the movement, they had always been able to forget any bad thing that had happened or any threat that loomed. Talking about nothing in particular or not talking at all, watching the countryside roll by, singing old songs. And for Clyde, watching Bonnie sleep—which was almost inevitable after a few hours, no matter what kind of a bind they were in— always filled his heart with a simple and indescribable kind of peace.

She opened her eyes just outside of Nashville, tousled and curious. They drove into the city, followed the road along the waterfront and rolled by the façade of a stately hotel called The Hermitage.

"This here's the place for us, Clyde," she said. "Let's waste some of Sal's money tonight."

Clyde pulled over just past the hotel so they could wrap the guns in a blanket. Then he threw it in reverse and, tires squealing, rocketed back to the entrance.

A valet in a red uniform surprised Bonnie by popping

out of the marbled front doorway to open her door, but she adjusted to the attention. Clutching the valise with the pistols and money, she let him help her out of the car.

The bellhop scurried around to the other side where Clyde waited.

"Your keys, sir?" he said, holding his hand out.

"Why the hell would I give you my keys?" Clyde asked.

"So I can park it for you," the young man said. He was nonplussed; hotel etiquette was not widespread.

"What's to prevent you from just driving off with it?"

"It's my job, sir," he said solemnly. "All our guests do it. You let the front desk know when you'll need it again, and I'll get it for you, quick as a whistle."

"You hearing this?" Clyde said to Bonnie.

"Guess it's the way things are done," she said. "Go on, give him the keys and a dollar for his trouble."

"I have to pay him to steal my car?" Clyde asked as he tossed his keys up high. The boy grabbed them out of the air. Clyde pulled out a dollar and pressed it into his hand. "You take real good care of that car now, you hear?" The bellhop nodded excitedly, overjoyed at the size of the tip, and slipped behind the wheel.

Bonnie put her arm in Clyde's and they ascended the grand entrance, walked into the ornate lobby foyer and up to the front desk.

"I want the best room you got for my gal," Clyde said, blustering to hide his nervousness at the unfamiliar lush setting, and pulling out a ten-dollar bill. "A bath tub with running water, electric lights, the whole shooting match."

"Of course, sir, all our rooms have electricity," the desk clerk said, looking over the registry. "The honeymoon suite is available for five dollars. Would it happen to be your honeymoon?"

"Naw," Clyde said. "Me and, uh, Brenda—we been married for a month of Sundays now. But we'll take it anyway, 'cuz it's always our honeymoon."

"May we help with your luggage, sir?" another bellhop asked.

"No thanks," Bonnie said, holding on tight to the valise.

"I meant your suitcases, in particular," the bellhop said.

"We got a little ahead of our luggage," Clyde said. "I'll be taking the missus shopping to make up for it."

It was the first time either of them had ever been in an elevator, and they looked at each other anxiously when the operator closed the metal door, trapping them in the tiny space. With a lurch, it clanked into motion, and Bonnie squeezed Clyde's hand as it rumbled up to the tenth floor. The bellhop led them down the carpeted hall and opened the door, ushering them inside the suite.

"Holy…" Bonnie said, catching herself.

The suite was huge, bigger than the houses they'd grown up in, with upholstered furniture in a sitting room, brocade coverings, and landscape oil paintings on every wall. The bellhop swung open the French doors to the bedroom, where a four-poster bed took up half the room. The balcony windows opened up onto the riverfront promenade.

Bonnie walked from room to room. "There are two bathrooms," she said.

"If this don't beat all," Clyde said. "Thank you, boy. Now how do I go about getting a bottle of hooch and maybe some bubbly?"

"I'll bring that right up for you, sir," the bellhop said. "Would you like some food?"

"Hell yeah. We've been driving all day."

The bellhop stood by the door, eyes averted, and waited, clearing his throat.

"Give him a tip, darling," Bonnie said.

"For doing his job?" Clyde grumbled, digging out another dollar.

The door shut behind him, and Clyde watched Bonnie dashing around in circles, taking in the grandeur and luxury. "It's beautiful," she said.

"Sure beats West Dallas," Clyde said.

Thirty minutes later there was a knock at the door, and they both reached for their guns, but it was just the waiter. He wheeled in a cart laden with oysters, cheese, ham, chicken, bread, and crackers, along with champagne on ice and a bottle of Kentucky bourbon.

"You'd never know there was a Depression going on," said Clyde to the young man as he spread a crisp, white linen tablecloth over the dining table and arranged the food.

"Certainly not at The Hermitage, sir," he said.

"What am I supposed to do with this?" Bonnie asked, holding up an oyster.

"Typically, people swallow them whole. Not the shell, of course," the waiter said, without missing a beat. "Oysters are reputed to have certain, shall we say, aphrodisiac effects."

"Show us how," Clyde said, as he belted back a shot of whiskey.

"I'm sure that would be inappropriate," the young man said, tugging at his starched collar.

He handed the boy a dollar, and the server lost no time selecting an oyster from the platter and slurping it down. He gagged and then mumbled an apology. "They've never been much to my liking."

"I think I'll stick to chicken," Clyde said, laughing.

"Let me try," Bonnie said, sliding an oyster from the shell into her mouth. She swallowed it whole, and then sat back thinking, eyes looking at the ceiling, her face quizzical. Clyde and the boy waited for her to say something.

"I do believe I'm already feeling that aphrodisiac effect you mentioned. Perhaps it's best you leave now," she said, winking at the boy. "Before it's too late."

As soon as the door shut behind him, Bonnie and Clyde laughed and then tore into the food, washing it down with champagne.

There was another knock, and they both reached for their guns again, but it was only the desk clerk. Three women stood behind him with a rack of clothes.

"Mr. Prentiss, I am sorry to disturb you but I overheard you mention your wife is in need of some clothes. I took the liberty of ringing our in-house seamstress and asking her to show some outfits that may be of interest. May we come in?"

Clyde looked back at Bonnie, who was standing with her mouth open, staring at the clothes. "I think that might be okay," he said.

The women filed in with racks of dresses, scarves, and coats. Bonnie rifled through the garments, pointing to the ones she liked. They measured, cut, and fit Bonnie with six new outfits as Clyde looked on approvingly, sipping whiskey.

"Don't forget the, uh, nighttime clothes," he said. "You know, for sleeping, um, between couples. Married couples."

"Of course, sir. We have the latest styles from Paris," said the seamstress. Bonnie fondled the satin and silks and picked out three negligees.

"I think I'd like to see that one modeled," Clyde said.

The seamstresses giggled in unison, collected their wares and backed out of the room, but not before Clyde gave each of them a dollar. He was getting comfortable in the big spender role.

Bonnie finished her glass of champagne, picked up the bottle by its neck and dangled a pink negligee in front of Clyde.

"Come on then, Clarence, follow me into the boudoir," she said, drawing out the last syllable and slurring a little.

He looked up as if confirming with God that he was in heaven. "I sure could get used to this," he said, following her into the bedroom.

CHAPTER 12

The mayor of Hooverville

The sunrise woke Bonnie, shining through the tenth-floor windows, and she pulled a pillow over her eyes. Maybe it was the oysters, or the booze, or the view, or the obscenely soft bed, or a combination of all that, but they had made love long into the night, and now she felt lazy and satisfied.

Reveling in the clean sheets, she burrowed deeper and threw her arms around Clyde. Still half-asleep, he snorted from under the blankets, instinctively reaching out for her and pulling her close. She kissed his neck, taking in the salty taste of his sweat, and then gently disentangled herself from his arms.

Bonnie slid out of bed and tiptoed into the bathroom. She turned on the gold-plated faucet. Water poured into the clawfoot tub as she peeled off the bandages from her leg and then eased into the scented, soapy bath. The tub felt as big as a swimming pool, and she stretched out and closed her eyes.

She knew it was better to put it all out of her mind, soldier forward, enjoy the money, and elbow their way to chumping that assassin. Still, she couldn't keep herself from thinking back over the conversations with Sal, looking for hints about who she was and what kind of long con she had going.

Clyde sandwiched his head between two pillows to drown out the sound of running water but slowly rose up to consciousness anyway. He looked around the room, sorting out the details from the night before—the empty champagne bottles, the negligee hanging on the back of a chair, his fedora on the lampshade—and grinned.

He waited awhile before entering the bathroom, wanting to give her time to soak. When he did, he looked down on her, so beautiful, eyes closed, and her breasts just visible through the sudsy water; it took his breath away. Bonnie felt his gaze, and her eyes fluttered open.

She blew him a kiss, and he smiled.

"You look all serious," Clyde said. "What are you thinking about in that water?"

"Clyde, what do you think Sal meant when she said every man wanted to be you, and every woman wished they were me?"

"Does it matter?" Clyde said, turning to look in the mirror and splashing cold water on his face.

"So many people came to my funeral," she said. "Do you think we squandered all that fame?"

"I ain't following you," he said.

"We didn't use it for anything. Just got ourselves shot up and bungled a bunch of robberies," she said.

"What would we have used it for?" he asked. "We were famous on account of the bad things we done."

His tone made clear to Bonnie it was not a subject he was interested in pursuing.

"Never mind. Hand me one of them fluffy towels. Better yet, make it two. I need souvenirs," she said, sitting up. "And get the kitchen to pack us some ham sandwiches and beer. It's time to go."

Later, looking in the mirror, Bonnie admired the new purple skirt and collared matching pill jacket with a sleeveless, black turtleneck shirt. But the part of the outfit she liked best was the silk stockings. The burn scars had healed enough to tolerate the fabric, and she marveled at their smoothness.

"My legs never felt so good," she whispered to Clyde, as they walked down the corridor to the elevator. "Just touch them." Clyde happily obliged and put his hand on her thigh and smiled as she shivered when he dragged his finger higher.

"I would've thought you got enough last night," she said.

"I can't get enough of you, Bon," he said. "Ever."

"Who is this Bon?" she asked, swatting his hand away. "My name is Brenda, and I'm jealous as all get-out."

Clyde laughed, and Bonnie felt a flush of happiness at the sound. If only things could go on like this forever; if only they'd been like this before.

The bellhops had boxed up Bonnie's new wardrobe along with bag lunches and were packing it all into the back seat, unwittingly placing the packages on top of the hidden rifles.

Her purse was loaded down with hotel matches, soap, and two ashtrays. Clyde teased her with her stolen "souvenirs," but she ignored him. "We already paid for them," she said. "No point being wasteful."

They drove out of Nashville. The sun lavished its late-morning beams through the windshield, and Bonnie pulled on sunglasses.

"That was sure something else," Bonnie said, settling into the passenger side. "I can hardly believe people live like that."

She turned to Clyde. He was still wearing the suit Sal had given him. "We're gonna have to find you some clothes to match up to our new status," she said. "You're all rumpled."

"We'll see about that," he said.

The steady vibration of the tires against the asphalt put them in a familiar trance, pulling and stretching their contented mood over and around the passing terrain. Bonnie watched the countryside glide by, moving her hand like a wind sail up and down outside of the car window.

"Clyde," she said.

"Yeah, baby?"

"After we get to New York City and take care of the three barons, I want you to promise me something, okay?"

"The three barons?" he asked.

"That's what I've been calling those cabbage farmers in my head," she said.

"Can a lady be a baron?" he asked. "Don't that make her a bassinet or something?"

"The two barons and the baroness just don't have the same ring," she said. "But the more important thing is the promise you're about to make me."

"Baby," he said, "you know if it's my power to give or to get, I'll hand it to you on a silver platter."

"I want you to take me to the Empire State Building."

"That's it?" he asked. "That's easy. I promise."

"And I wouldn't mind staying in another fancy hotel."

Miles later, with the tank close to empty, they pulled into a Gulf gas station on the edge of Roanoke. Clyde stretched as he got out of the car. A short man in greasy coveralls was sleeping in a beat-up metal chair tilted against the station wall. He bolted up when they drove in and unhinged the single gasoline pump.

"Fill 'er up," Clyde said, pulling out a dollar bill.

"Where's the ladies room?" Bonnie asked, emerging from the car and straightening her new clothes.

"Around the left side of the station," said the man,

handing her the key. "Be sure to lock it up."

"Lock it? Who are you expecting in these lonely parts?" she asked.

"We've got plenty of no-accounts to worry about round here," he said, tipping his head toward the opposite side of the station. "Wouldn't want no trouble for a high-class young lady like yourself."

"Thanks for looking out for me," she said. Clyde threw her a sideways glance at the flirtatious tone in her voice. Both he and the mechanic watched the sway of her hips as she walked away.

The mechanic poked each tire to check the pressure, and then used a wet rag to clean the dead bugs and road grime off the headlights and windshield.

In the bathroom, Bonnie freshened her deep red lipstick and smoothed out her hair, still getting used to her blonde bob.

The hinge on the door squeaked as she closed it behind her, and the rough, wooden edge caught on the black stockings at her left calf. She swore, knowing the run would take hold and travel up the entire leg in minutes, ruining her first pair of honest-to-God silk stockings.

The man was finishing up but Clyde was no longer next to the car. She called his name but he didn't answer. The gas jockey pointed to the other side of the station. Bonnie walked over and found Clyde on the edge of a dusty field, hands thrust deep in his pockets and his hat cocked low, looking out over a sight they'd seen too many times.

Hundreds of homeless people were crowded together in a degraded cornfield. Barefoot children ran around the shantytown of makeshift cardboard and plywood homes, tents, pallets on the ground, automobiles without wheels, and broken-down furniture. Groups huddled quietly around a smattering of cook fires. It looked to Bonnie like they were trying to make soup out of the dried-up husks and stalks.

"Another damn Hooverville," Clyde said.

Like stuttering moths to a flame, men and women began to move toward Bonnie and Clyde, casting hungry, sunken eyes on Clyde's shiny leather shoes and Bonnie's fancy dress, as if no longer able to imagine a world where such things were possible.

"Might as well give these poor saps our food," Clyde said.

They retrieved the hotel-packed food from the car's back seat and walked the dusty footpaths between the tents and cardboard shelters, handing out the sandwiches and cookies. The downtrodden, half-clothed people swarmed, snatching and grabbing at the treasure. Some ate immediately; others gave the food to the skin-and-bones children or the elderly. Still others looked at them with heartbroken faces when they realized they were too late.

Near the center of the encampment, a tall, lanky man stopped them. His jacket was ripped at the elbow and too small for his frame. "I'm the mayor of this establishment," he said.

"Mayor?" Clyde asked. "Of this shit hole?"

"It may be a shit hole, but we try to keep order here, take care of the women and children as best we can, take a little pride until things turn around."

Bonnie felt something on her leg. A little girl with matted red hair and dirt ground into her hollowed cheeks ran her fingers up and down Bonnie's leg, tracing the run in her stocking, intrigued by the softness of the silk and emboldened by youth. Her mother called out for her to stop pestering the nice lady, but her voice was tired and lacked conviction.

Bonnie dug out the last cookie from the bag and pressed into the girl's hand. "Here you go, darling," she said. The child's eyes went wide with joy, and she ran back to her mother.

"The cops let you stay here?" Clyde asked.

"They don't want us in town," the mayor said. "Makes the place look bad, I suppose. Trashy, they said."

"Is any help coming for you people?" Bonnie asked the mayor.

"We're all waiting on the jobs President Roosevelt promised."

The mayor looked over at the shiny new car by the gas pump.

"You folks are not from around here."

"Passing through," Bonnie said.

"Name's Prentiss," Clyde said. "Newlyweds."

"Hope you have better luck than us," the mayor said.

"It'll get better soon," Clyde said, slipping a five-dollar bill into his hand. "Get some food in them young ones. The country is gonna need them healthy when things turn around."

The mayor nodded and returned to his city hall, a rocking chair under an oily tarp, and watched as Bonnie and Clyde walked up the hill toward the station.

Clyde pulled the car back onto the county road.

"First the honeymoon suite, now you're calling us newlyweds?" Bonnie said. "Clyde, you got something you want to ask me?"

Clyde smiled halfheartedly but did not respond. Bonnie unfolded the map, tracing the route to New York.

They drove through the night. A full moon hung low in the dark sky against a dusting of stars as if daring the sun to rise, and the still lit-up New York City skyline came into view. Clyde eased the car into the line of traffic snaking through the Holland Tunnel, adjusting his eyes to the steady stream of headlights passing him in the opposite direction. Bonnie held her ears to soften the reverberating noise and car honking inside the tunnel.

After they passed into Manhattan, Clyde drove around for a while, and they both took in the early morning crowds, the smells, and the frenetic activity.

"Don't these people ever sleep?" Bonnie said, feeling herself already getting caught up in the electric energy of the city.

He circled uptown and then back, ending up around Times Square. Vagrants filled the streets. A few cops, mixed with a handful of well-dressed women and men, walked by quickly, eyes averted. Boarded-up theaters and shops stood next to saloons and brothels.

"Well, not much like the pictures we seen from New Year's," Bonnie said.

"It's on the downslope," Clyde said.

"I been thinking about our next step," Bonnie said.

"Yeah?" Clyde said.

"We have to bring them three barons out into the open," she said.

"How we gonna do that?"

"We're gonna do what we do best," Bonnie said. "We're gonna rob a bank."

CHAPTER 13

Making a rather large withdrawal

"This here the place?" Clyde asked.

After wandering around the city in awe, reining in the lavish spending by half, and trading champagne for martinis, they slept at the Algonquin Hotel. Now they sat in their car, looking up at an imposing granite and pink marble building—the First Independent Bank of New York.

"It'll surely do," Bonnie said.

"Ain't it something?" he whistled. "It's the biggest goddamn bank I've ever seen. Must be a lot of money in there." He reached into the back seat and dug under the blanket for one of the BARs. "Well, let's get to robbing it," he said. "See if we can't catch the eye of Mr. Stubbs."

"Hold on, Clyde," Bonnie said, catching his arm. "We can't just waltz into the biggest damn bank in New York, guns blazing, like we was knocking over some Podunk bank in the middle of Kansas. This here's New York City. Look around."

He pushed his hat back and peered out the side window. "There's an awful lot of people, that's for sure. And cars."

"We've never robbed a bank when we couldn't see the city limits from where we stood," she said. "I don't think we could get out of this town alive with a map and a two-day head start."

"I wouldn't bet against us in a running gun battle," Clyde said.

"Me either, when it comes right down to it, but we need to start being smart about things if we want to get out of this alive." She lit a cigarette.

"You got one of your ideas?" he asked.

"I'm working on one."

She tapped her fingernails on the armrest and looked up and down the city block, then smiled.

"You see that little diner next to the bank? Let's go get a piece of pie and a cup of coffee." He looked at her curiously. "Bring your pistol," she said.

The bell above the door jangled when they walked in, rousing the waitress from her reveries over a Hollywood scandal sheet by the cash register. They were the only customers, and she brightened at the thought of a tip, no matter how small. "Sit anywhere you like, folks."

They slid into a booth near the front and ordered two cups of coffee and two slices of pie—pecan for Bonnie and apple with a scoop of butter brickle ice cream for Clyde.

"I don't know how it'll end, but I sure like how your bank-robbing plan starts," Clyde said, taking a bite of pie and washing it down with a swallow of black coffee.

She took a small bite of her pie but then pushed it away. "See that auto shop across the street?"

He nodded.

"Go get us a can of gasoline."

"The tank is damn near full," he said.

"You trust me?"

"Completely."

"Then please do what I'm asking."

He took another big bite of his pie, wiped his mouth with his sleeve, layering pie crumbs on the caked mustard already stained there, and then stood and straightened his hat. He took a few steps, but then turned back and stooped to take a hurried bite out of her pie slice as well.

"The pie will be here when you get back," Bonnie said.

"My guess is there won't be much time for eating when I get back," he said.

"Clyde, don't hurt anybody over there," she said.

She stirred a sugar cube into her coffee and watched him saunter across the street and return a few minutes later with a jerry can full of gas. As he walked in, the waitress looked up from biting her thumbnail. "I don't think you ought to be bringing that in here."

"It's okay," he said. "It's part of the plan." He plopped it down on the table and took a bite of apple pie. "The ice cream is all melted."

"Seriously," the waitress said, then turned and yelled into the kitchen. "Frank, he just brought in a gas can."

"You can't have that in here, folks," Frank said, as he came out of the kitchen through the swinging doors, wiping his palms on a striped apron. "It'll stink the place up." He walked up to the table and stood, hands on his hips as Bonnie smiled up at him. "Well, what are you going to do about it?" he asked.

"Frank, I'm sorry to say, we're about to make your day real bad. Cl…arence, hand me a gun."

Clyde pulled his .45 out of his belt and slid it across the table. She picked it up and cocked it, pointing it at Frank. "I need you and the gal to sit down in the booth across from me here, be quiet, and do what we ask."

Her tone was so even and so conversational they didn't feel scared. They just sat down at the booth.

"What are you gonna do?" Frank asked. "There isn't any money. You're the only customers all day."

"Remember I said you should be quiet," Bonnie said. "Clarence, the door." She tilted her head. "Go flip the sign. And then find something to tie them up with."

He returned with a role of tape and bound their wrists behind their backs.

"Please don't kill us," Frank said.

"We don't intend to," Bonnie said. "But tell me, you got this place insured?"

Frank nodded.

"Good," Bonnie said. "Clarence, tip that gas over in the kitchen and drop a match on it. I'm gonna take Frank and…" She looked at the waitress.

"Dolores."

"I'm gonna take Frank and Dolores out to the car and stash them. Things are about to get hotter than a three-dollar pistol in here."

A few minutes later, Bonnie and Clyde were standing by their car. Frank and Dolores were in the back seat out of sight, rags stuffed in their mouths.

Smoke began to billow out of the front of the building, and shouts went up from bystanders. It wasn't long before fire trucks arrived.

As the firemen rolled up, Bonnie and Clyde ran up the steps into the bank next door against the stream of customers and employees alike, who were filing out to investigate the source of the commotion.

"Stay here and keep an eye on him," she whispered to Clyde as they passed the security guard, an older man with a thick gray mustache and a revolver on his hip. "And no killing."

Bonnie made a beeline to the side of the teller line where one girl was watching her friends push through the gate and hurry toward the ornate front doors. Bonnie caught the gate and the elbow of the girl just as she was finally ready to pass through, and pulled her back behind the counter.

"Honey, I'm real sorry about this," Bonnie said, flashing the gun. "I'm going to need you to give me some money. A lot of money."

"Who do you think you are, Bonnie Parker?" the girl asked, a little breathless at the thought.

"Something like that, and don't get fresh with me," Bonnie said, pulling the gun from her waistband. "How much money do you have around?"

"Not much," the girl said, and Bonnie pinched her arm. She squeaked and shot a nervous, sideways look at the open vault.

"That's like leaving the candy store unattended when school gets out," Bonnie said. "Come on back with me."

She followed Bonnie into the vault.

"Is there a bag or something?" Bonnie asked.

"You didn't think this through much, did you?" the girl said. "How about one of these canvas bank bags?"

"That'll do nicely," Bonnie said.

"You can put the gun away," the girl said as Bonnie watched her stuff bundles of bills into the bag. "It's not my money."

When the bag was half-full, she hefted it. "How much do you think you can carry? You're tiny."

"Load it on up," Bonnie said. "I'll make do."

When the bag was stuffed full, the girl struggled to zip it closed and then used both hands to drop it at Bonnie's feet.

"You think what they pay you is fair?" Bonnie asked.

The girl shook her head. "Not really."

"Well, they're gonna blame this heist on me and my boyfriend out there. All of it. If a stack or two of hundreds ended up in your pockets, no one would be the wiser."

"Stealing is wrong," the girl said.

"Most of this money in here—probably all of it—was

stolen from some broke-down farmers or men somewhere who worked their whole lives thinking they was doing the right thing," Bonnie said. "Only when push came to shove them fat cats on Wall Street foreclosed on them fine people and took both the money and land. You tell me how that's not wrong."

"It probably is," the girl said, looking at the remaining cash.

"You do what you want," Bonnie said. "It'll be between you and the Lord. But don't poke your head out of here until me and my man are gone."

Bonnie saw Clyde still standing behind the guard, looking nervously at her. She nodded, and started out across the floor.

As she approached, a man in a suit pushed into the revolving door and saw her through the glass. His eyes flared, and he hollered, catching the attention of the guard and pointing emphatically behind him. The guard turned, saw Bonnie struggling with the large bag, and dropped his hand to the butt of his gun.

"Sorry, old timer," Clyde whispered. He pulled his hand out of his pocket and cracked the guard on the chin with brass knuckles, knocking him out, and then caught his body and gently laid him into the path of the revolving door, trapping the bank manager inside.

Clyde grabbed the money bag from Bonnie, tipped his hat at the manager, and they scooted out through the regular door into the crowd and jumped in their car.

Fifteen minutes later, they dumped Frank and Dolores on the sidewalk next to Central Park with their pockets full of hundred-dollar bills.

"Pretty good plan," Clyde said as they roared away. "Now what?"

"Now we figure out how to get noticed," Bonnie said.

CHAPTER 14

Wanted attention

Carrying sodas, they walked beneath the ornately carved stone arch of Washington Square. Bonnie looked up and squinted her eyes. "What's it say?" she asked, pointing to the top.

Clyde strained to see the words on the last level of the curved structure. "Can't make out the first part, but the second part says, 'The event is in the hand of God.'"

"Isn't that the truth," Bonnie said, laughing loudly, still feeling a manic high from the heist.

"Seems we come to the right place," Clyde said, pointing to a bench near the edge of the square.

They sat down and watched the people pass by, letting the peak of adrenaline from the robbery wear off. Men in suits rushed through the park, hurrying to meet deadlines and obligations. Young women pushed prams. A man in the corner played a flute. An artist pondered an easel. Pigeons pecked at garbage around the circular fountain.

Clyde took a sip to make some room in the bottle, ripped the corner from a package of peanuts and shook them into the drink. He opened another package and held it out for Bonnie, and she tilted her bottle so he could fill it as well.

"Now what?" she asked.

"Now we drink this before the peanuts get soggy," he

said, tipping the bottle up and enjoying the salty, fizzy, crunchy combination.

"I meant, how do we make sure them three barons know we're the ones who stole their money?"

He looked at her sideways, eyebrows arched, then pulled her in close. A crowd of schoolgirls ran by; one trailed an orange kite above. The children laughed and screamed as the kite nosedived into the water fountain.

"I think that'll be the easy part, Bon," he said. "My guess is people like that, people who love money more than life, they'll keep their ears to the ground—hell, someone else's ears—to make sure they get it back."

"You can't listen to a whole town the size of New York," she said.

"It's like hunting quail," Clyde said. "You don't listen for what sounds the same. You let that just wash over you. You have to listen for what sounds different. We need to make the right kind of noise, a different noise, and loud enough so they can't miss it."

"Baby, you're not making any sense," she said. "I don't know what you're going on about, but I love you something fierce right now."

She kissed him. He slipped his hand around her waist and tucked his finger in the band of her skirt and behind her stockings, feeling bare skin.

"What I'm going on about is showing you a good time like this old city ain't never seen before," he said. "Let's find us someplace with one of them champagne fountains, and maybe a movie star or two."

"I like the sounds of this plan," Bonnie said.

One of the schoolgirls shrieked when she dropped the string to the downed kite. The girls leaned over the edge of the fountain, watching the kite dance in the water, out of reach.

"Help them little girls get their kite out of the water, would you Clyde?"

"You want me to wade in there?"

"Please, baby? They're too young to be already disappointed by life."

Clyde leaned down to untie his shoes. "The things I do for you, girl," he said, rolling his pants up.

Later that evening, after stashing their bag of tricks and stolen money at the Algonquin, they made their way to the Moonlight Room, a club not far from the address Sal gave them for the palatial Dunthorpe home. The place was hopping, with a band playing swing jazz and young men and women dancing, flirting, laughing, and shouting.

Bonnie's eyes lit up at the sight of the dancers shimmying and shaking, swinging one another around, and jitterbugging, and waving their hands in the air. "Come on baby, let's dance," she yelled over the music.

"I don't know what kind of dancing this is. I'll look like a real dead-footer out there," he said.

"Isn't that a good way to get us noticed?" she said, already tapping her foot to the beat.

"Hold on," he said, and she watched him navigate through the crowd to reach the band. When the song ended, he caught the attention of the bandleader—a handsome man with a klieg light for a smile and carefully slicked-back hair—and motioned him close for a confab.

The man bent down, and Clyde whispered in his ear, but the bandleader shook his head and started to pull away. Clyde motioned for him to wait and reached deep inside his jacket. Knowing there was a .45 there, Bonnie feared the worst. But instead of a gun, Clyde pulled out a stack of bills and thrust them into the surprised man's hand.

The bandleader looked at the money, then turned to his band and grinned, slipping the money out of sight.

"Folks," he said, cradling the microphone like a lover. "We're gonna change it up a little and play some Western swing tonight."

The crowd booed.

"No hillbilly music," someone yelled.

Clyde, scowling, hopped onto the stage and pulled the microphone toward him. "Me and my gal are new to town, and we just made a big score. We want to hear some real music, some Western music, and I'm willing to do whatever it takes," he shouted.

"Go back to the farm, hicks," someone yelled.

"Rubes," a woman shouted.

"On account of the inconvenience, I'm buying the next round for everyone in the joint." He waved a twenty-dollar bill. "Actually, the next three rounds."

The room erupted into cheers, and the bandleader got the band refocused. Soon enough, a swinging version of "Cotton-Eyed Joe" had the place back in a dancing groove. Clyde made his way to Bonnie, stopping long enough to toss the money to a surprised bartender and pick up two coupes of champagne.

"Now this is music you can dance to," he said, handing one to Bonnie. "Drink up. We're about to trip the light fantastic." They clinked glasses, downed the champagne, and then set them on the table. With a grin, he caught her by the waist and swung her around onto the slippery dance floor.

An hour later, they were danced out and left by the back door for some fresh air. Just as Bonnie was lighting a cigarette in the alley behind the club, three men came out of the shadows.

"Right on time," Clyde whispered, sizing them up. On either side, two hulks who could be cousins, they looked so much alike, each looming tall over Clyde with likely a hundred pounds on him. In the middle stood a younger man, smaller, about Clyde's size, with oiled black hair, cold eyes, and a toothpick in the corner of his mouth.

"You the hayseeds dropping all the money?" Toothpick asked.

"What's it to you?" Clyde said, taking a step forward. Bonnie dropped back.

"Depends where you got that cash," Toothpick said. "Could mean the difference between a beating and a murder."

"What if I told you it fell off a truck, at the intersection of You're-all-wet Boulevard and Kiss-off Avenue," Clyde snarled.

One of the hulking men opened his coat and swung up a sawed-off, double-barreled shotgun. He ratcheted the hammers back.

Toothpick smiled and slipped an ice pick out of his breast pocket. "Murder it is, then, Country Wheat."

CHAPTER 15

Getting historical

Royce was waiting outside the Dallas Historical Society when it opened, a thermos of coffee under his arm and a fresh notebook in hand. He flashed his press credentials and asked for access to the Bonnie and Clyde archive.

The volunteer staffing the desk, an older woman with a towering beehive, looked at the thermos. "You can't take beverages into the archives room," she said, her tone suggesting the eighth deadly sin was about to be committed. "You'll have to leave that in a locker, which you can rent for twenty-five cents." She pointed at the lockers behind him.

He checked his pockets. "Do you have change for a dollar?" he asked.

She tapped a sign taped to the desk: No Change. "We can sell you this commemorative Dallas Historical Society pencil for seventy-five cents."

After he put the thermos away, he signed in—with his new pencil—and she led him to the archive room. "It's the largest collection of Bonnie and Clyde materials in the world," she said.

"I'd like to focus on the photos of the bodies," Royce said. "Also, I'd like to see all known receipts, telegrams, letters, and any other materials associated with the funeral fifty years ago."

The woman nodded. "Bonnie's mother provided us with copies of all that. And those newspaper boys back then in the 30s were all over this story. Their sales skyrocketed anytime Bonnie and Clyde were in the paper. They gave us a lot for the archives too."

"When did Bonnie's mother donate what she had?"

"Right before she died in 1944," she said.

"She wasn't in prison then?"

"No. She died in her home. I don't believe she was ever in prison," the woman said.

She left him at a long, low table—the only person in the deathly silent room—and he began sorting and sifting through mountains of photos, receipts, letters, and microfiche files. Four hours later, he was bleary-eyed and disappointed.

After reclaiming his coffee and making a show of drinking it in the lobby, he ate a French dip sandwich at the café down the street and then made the long drive back to Lubbock. During the drive, he wondered when Bonnie figured out her mother wasn't in prison or whether or not by keeping their end of the bargain, Sal let her go. Or maybe she had never been in prison at all.

Most everyone was gone by the time he got back to the newsroom, except for two reporters banging away on typewriters, the janitor slowly wheeling the cleaning cart from office to office, and Terrence, the eager intern who had waited specifically for Royce to return.

Royce leaned back in his swivel chair, the joints squeaking in protest, and propped his scruffy cowboy boots up on the desk. He'd already filed his articles—an obituary for the head of the school board and the results of the high school football game—the day before, so he opened the bottom drawer of the desk and reached for the bottle of whiskey.

Terrence came in, brimming with an annoying kind of enthusiasm. Royce groaned in his mind and put the whiskey back and closed the drawer. No reason to kill the boy's idealism this early in his life, he thought.

"How was your trip to Dallas?" Terrence asked, making it sound far away and exotic.

"Long and fruitless," Royce said. "Why are you still here? Everyone else is long gone."

"I wanted to personally deliver the results of the identity searches you requested," Terrence said.

"Okay, go on," Royce said, grinning despite himself at Terrence's youthful energy.

"First, the three people from the 1930s—he looked down at his notebook—Percival Stubbs, Angela Dunthorpe, and Archibald Farquist," he said.

"Yeah? Are they real?" Royce asked.

"Most definitely. Although all three are no longer living," Terrence said. "Mr. Stubbs was a banker, and I have confirmed Miss Dunthorpe was a steel heiress. I am still waiting for information on Mr. Farquist, but he did live in New York during the years you asked about."

"Okay, not proof, and easy to lie about, but something," Royce said.

"I am not lying," Terrence said, nervously.

"Not you, kid—a source," Royce said. "What about the other stuff?"

Terrence handed Royce a single sheet of white paper, and Royce scanned it quickly. No marriage certificate, no social security numbers, no birth records, nothing. It was as if they had never existed.

"But there must be someone in this country with the names Clarence or Brenda Prentiss?"

"Yes, of course, sir," Terrence said with as much gravity as he could muster. "But none that live anywhere near each other. A Clarence in California, a Brenda in Connecticut. None in Texas," said the teenager.

The young man stood erect in his starched white shirt, proud of what he hoped had been solid newspaper investigative work, looking for approval.

"Then who the hell did I see her bury?" he asked.

"Sir?" Terrence asked.

Royce sighed; expectations exhausted him. "What did the FBI say?"

"They didn't answer."

"How many times did you ask?"

"I faxed four requests to their main line and called three times."

That's a little odd, Royce thought. Not conspiracy-theory odd, but unusual.

"We should check the deed papers, see which bank owns the mortgage," he said, reaching for a notepad.

"I already did, sir," Terrence said. He handed Royce a second sheet. "There is no mortgage on the house or the land. It was a cash transaction."

"Whose name is on the deed?" Royce asked. "Someone has to own the damn place."

Terrence handed Royce a third sheet of paper. "The house and land are not owned by a person. It belongs to something called the National Grange of the Order of Patrons of Husbandry."

"The Grange? The Grange owns the house?"

Terrence nodded. "And the land."

"Guess I'll be driving out to talk to Brenda tomorrow," he said, reaching for the desk drawer and the whiskey. Enthusiasm be damned.

CHAPTER 16

Never forget the ladies

Clyde stared down the twin barrels of the sawed-off shotgun, big as two train tunnels at this close range and twice as murderous, and began to laugh.

The three men looked at him, and then at one another, in disbelief, thinking this wiry little man had lost his mind, until the ratchet of metal—the hammer of a pistol being cocked—brought them back into the moment.

It was Bonnie. She was standing behind them, pressing the muzzle of a sleek little .38 against the back of Toothpick's skull.

"You always forget about the ladies," she said. "Think we're just shrinking violets—that we're going to faint dead away. Honestly, it's embarrassing."

Toothpick dropped his ice pick and held his hands out like he was trying to find his balance on a high wire in gusting winds.

"Let's everybody just calm down, darling," he said. "There's no reason anyone has to die."

"You may have to die," Bonnie said, jabbing him in the head again. "For calling me darling. And for all that talk about murdering. And also because your goon is still covering my man. If that other big boy reaches inside his coat or you shoot my fella, I'm gonna put one through your skull. And then I'm gonna put two into the back of shotgun-boy over there."

"Keep him covered," Toothpick said, calmly. "Seems we are at a standoff, because he's gonna cut handsome Jack in half."

"Ain't gonna happen like that," Clyde said, swatting the gun to the side. With a startled oath, the thug pulled the trigger, but it was too late. The gun roared and blew holes in a tin trashcan beside them, sending it skipping down the alley.

"You got too close," Clyde said. "Rookie mistake and probably your last." He stepped forward, familiar brass knuckles on his fist, and hit the goon hard across the jaw. The metal shattered the man's teeth and split his lips like a ripe banana. He fell to the cement with a groan and lay unmoving. Bonnie watched with a mixture of awe and fear. Clyde liked hitting people a little too much.

Never slowing his momentum, Clyde bent and scooped up the ice pick and jammed it up and under Toothpick's kneecap, twisting it savagely so the handle broke off. Toothpick howled and fell back onto his ass, clutching his hands over the protruding metal spike.

Bonnie swung the gun around to the third man, who hadn't moved.

"You folks are not very good at this," she said.

"Yes ma'am," he said, fearing a bullet.

"Ma'am," Clyde repeated. "I like you. What's your name?"

"Eugene."

"Eugene, something tells me you're gonna make it through the night unscathed, long as you throw these other two into the trunk of our car and help us get them boys back to their rightful owners."

Clyde slipped out his .45, the jovial smile disappearing under an icy cold frown. "But don't think just because I like you, I won't kill you. I've killed people I like a lot more than you."

He stepped close to Bonnie, pulled her up to him by the small of her back, and kissed her. Bonnie could feel the heat coming from him. Violence always made him want to get close.

"Thanks for saving my bacon, baby. I'll show my appreciation later," he said. "Now run get the car and back it up here."

Ten minutes later, they were rumbling through the back streets of New York. Eugene drove and Bonnie sat behind him with her gun to his neck. Clyde was in the passenger seat, hat in his lap and head out the window enjoying the sights and sounds of New York. The other two were hog-tied in the trunk.

"You taking us to whoever sent you?"

"Yeah," Eugene said.

"Where we headed?" Clyde asked.

"The Brass Ring," Eugene said. "They meet there every Tuesday night for a late dinner and drinks."

"It's not a trap, is it?" Bonnie asked. "Because we'll make you walk in there first."

Eugene tightened his knuckles on the wheel and swerved to avoid a horse-drawn carriage. "I'm not gonna lie to you, on account of I want to live and all, and maybe find a new line of work," he said. "There's a lot of help there. Help with, you know, heaters."

Clyde checked his vest pocket and nodded. "I appreciate you leveling with us," he said, winking at Bonnie.

Eugene slowed the car and pointed at the discreet entrance of a restaurant. "That's the Brass Ring," he said. "Should I head around back?"

"Right up front is good," Clyde said.

When the car stopped, Clyde hopped out. "Step lightly, Eugene. Help me dump them right out on the curb."

Bonnie kept the gun on Eugene.

Toothpick gagged, cursed, and moaned. The other goon was still unconscious; Clyde wasn't very big, but there was a lot of rage behind his punches. With the two men laid out on the sidewalk, blocking the entrance, Bonnie and Clyde looked at Eugene.

"I'm just going to say it again—please don't kill me," Eugene said.

"Want me to tell you why you ain't punctured or dead?" Clyde asked.

Eugene nodded.

"Because you were respectful of my gal. That's what saved you. Now get on out of here. And maybe don't hang around with unsavory types."

Without another word, Eugene turned and trotted up the street and out of sight.

"You're a regular Tom Mix," Bonnie said. "Since when did we start wearing white hats?"

He smiled and puffed out his chest and adjusted his fedora. "Let's settle for gray. Ready for this, darling?"

"What's the plan?" she asked.

"We're going to let them know we're just the right kind of crazy to maybe be useful to them. And then sniff around until we can finger the assassin, then put them all in pine boxes and earn our angel wings and shake a leg someplace new and far away."

"Not far-fetched at all," she said.

"Got a better plan?" he asked.

"Nope. Let's go."

He walked up to the front doors, pulled them open, and they entered a velvet-draped sanctuary. Well-heeled diners dressed to the nines ate by candlelight at intimate tables. Crystal goblets and china and fine silverware clinked. Conversation was murmured and earnest. A band played quietly in the background.

"May I help you?" the maître de asked, looking askance at Clyde's dusty, rumpled clothes. Bonnie smoothed out her plaid skirt, one of the outfits from Nashville.

Clyde scanned the room until he saw them—two men and a woman dining in a private area partially screened off by thick red drapes.

"We're here to see some friends," Clyde said. "And there they are."

He crossed the dining room confidently, his limp giving him a rolling gait like he was heading downhill. Bonnie, lighter on her feet, stayed a few steps behind. The manager followed, hissing and snapping his fingers and trying to draw attention to the interlopers.

"Howdy," Clyde said, pushing his way into the private room, surprising the diners and a bodyguard standing near the back wall. The man reached for a gun under his jacket, but Clyde was faster, slipping out his pistol.

"Don't do nothing stupid," he said, cocking it.

The older of the two men looked at him, perturbed, but kept eating his Waldorf salad. "I think something stupid has already been done," he said.

Clyde thought about the pictures Sal had showed them. This was Stubbs, with great mutton-chop whiskers and a rounded belly from expensive eating and a sedentary life behind a desk.

Bonnie dragged in a chair and sat down, pulling out her revolver. "Mind if I have some bread?" she asked. "I'm starving."

"Please, help yourself," the woman said, smiling tightly. "We were just going to throw it away."

This, of course, was Angela Dunthorpe, Bonnie thought. She was prettier than Sal's picture made her out to be.

"I hear you been looking for us," Clyde said.

"I hear you took something that doesn't belong to you," Stubbs said.

"Your money, you mean? I don't think it belongs to you, either."

"It was in my bank."

"All that money, though. Hard not to think of it like a stray dog. Maybe it was looking for someone who could treat it better."

"I don't think you know who we are," the other man said.

This would be Farquist, Clyde thought. He was thin and jittery, with round spectacles and nervous hands.

"Correction. We don't care who you are," Clyde said. "It don't make no difference to us, one way or another."

"This bread is like eating silk," Bonnie said, unused to the taste of refined flour. "Darling, there's a bunch of guys headed this way. They look to mean business."

"I certainly hope they've got a little more starch than the last three you sent us," Clyde said. "Old Eugene was the only one with any fire in him, and the other two snuffed it out quick."

"What exactly did you hope to accomplish by coming here?" Stubbs asked.

"I was kind of hoping we could enjoy New York without having to look over our shoulders all the time. But I'm starting to think that's not going to happen."

"No, it's not. I don't think the rest of your night will be very pleasant, either," Stubbs said.

Clyde paused for an instant and looked at Bonnie. "Do you trust me?" he asked.

"Always," she said.

"This could go sideways fast," Clyde said.

"We're already dead. What difference does it make now?"

Clyde rocked back on his heels, then slipped a single

stick of TNT from his vest pocket and held the wick over the candle flame. It caught with an ominous hiss that trailed sparks down onto the white tablecloth.

"I think all our nights are about to take a detour straight into Shitsville," Clyde said.

There was a genuine gasp of terror from all three. Dunthorpe held her hand over her mouth, and Farquist tried to stand, but Clyde pointed the pistol at him. "Sit. It'll be over in a second."

"Stop this at once!" Stubbs shouted. "Be reasonable."

The fuse sputtered and died, and the smile on Clyde's face melted. "Well damn. That didn't work out very well."

Behind them came a chorus of Tommy guns being cocked.

CHAPTER 17

A bite to eat after a brush with death

Trussed up back-to-back, Bonnie and Clyde sat on their haunches, knees to chins, on the far side of the kitchen in the pantry area, stuffed between boxes of oysters on ice, pallets of flour sacks, and bags of potatoes.

Clyde was still out cold from a sap to the skull, and Bonnie was worried he was badly hurt. She kept gently wiggling and pushing into his back, trying to rouse him. But then a mouse ran across her foot, and she swore and kicked at it, her whole body jerking as it skittered away and burrowed into a flour sack.

The movement was enough to jar Clyde awake. He shook his head and looked around. "How long we been here?"

"Oh Clyde, thank the Lord, I was getting worried," she said. "We've been here about an hour. Seems like they're waiting until everyone is gone before they kill us. You okay?"

"My head is pounding like a prison work gang tromped across it, but I think I'm okay," he said.

"That was a fine show you put on out there. How did you fix the fuse to sputter out like that?"

"That's the crazy thing, Bon. I didn't. I was just gonna snuff it out or else throw it out the window. I was keeping it loose."

"Keeping it loose with dynamite?" she asked. "That's like the one time you ought not to keep it loose."

"Things have a way of working out for us," he said. He flexed his fingers, twisted and turned his wrists, and pulled his hands free with a flourish. "See? City folks couldn't keep a lazy mule tied up." With a quick look over his shoulder, he worried with her knots until the ropes also fell away to the floor.

The staff bustled around the restaurant kitchen, paying them no mind, the sight of bound strangers apparently a familiar one. Three men in starched shirts and chef's hats—their backs turned to Bonnie and Clyde—chopped, boiled, fried, and plated.

The smell of roasted turkey and baked apples hung sweet and savory in the air. Bonnie looked up at the ovens and counted seven birds cooling on the counter. A chef was carving the first one, placing the breast meat, wings, and crispy legs on a platter.

Two other men leaned over the sinks, washing dishes, cleaning up the plates, glasses, and silver from the diners.

"You hungry?" he asked.

"Peckish."

Clyde stood up and walked to the sinks, grabbed a hand towel, and snapped the wet rag against the backside of the biggest dishwasher. The man yowled and stopped washing, then turned around slowly. He loomed over Clyde.

"That smarts," he said slowly, rubbing his backside. "Why would you do that?"

Even from a distance, Bonnie could see the giant man didn't have his full senses. He stood big and stubborn like a just-built snowman, unable to put all the pieces together. About to berate his companion for slacking on the job, the second dishwasher—a smaller man but still taller than Clyde—turned, saw the stranger behind them, and dropped an armful of plates. The shattering crash caused the kitchen staff to look over.

Clyde didn't miss a beat.

"I'm mighty glad to get your attention, because my gal and I are hungrier than hell," he said. "Some of that delicious turkey would make a fine meal."

Clyde picked up a clean carving knife from the rack and casually flipped it around in his hand, making it clear he knew his way around a blade. He grabbed the smaller dishwasher, holding the knife against his throat, and pushed him toward the food. One of the cooks rushed through the swinging doors, exiting into the dining room, and Clyde knew he had only a few minutes.

"Now, don't nobody worry too much. What I want from you is a piece of turkey. You, son," he said to the giant dishwasher. "Grab some turkey and give it to my girl here."

"Don't hurt my friend," the big man said.

"Get the goddamned turkey, Lenny," the small man in Clyde's grasp yelled to the giant.

Lenny grabbed a serving tray and held it out to her.

"Where are your manners, hoss?" Clyde said. "Don't make her pick it up with her sweet, dainty hands."

"Oh Clyde, I don't mind," Bonnie said, standing and picking up a leg. She ripped off a tender piece and chewed it slowly, savoring the taste, and then picked off a strip of crispy skin and popped it in her mouth. "It's my favorite part," she said. "Clyde, you want some? It's good."

"You are gonna be in a shitload of trouble," said the head chef, holding a cleaver at the ready.

Bonnie held the leg up to Clyde's mouth so he could bite off a chunk.

"That is good," he said, juice trickling down his chin.

The dishwasher wriggled under his grasp, and Clyde pushed the blade closer to his throat. "Careful. We don't want no accidents now, do we?"

The kitchen door burst open, and Eugene entered, flanked by two even larger goons holding Tommy guns at hip level.

"Eugene? Now here we thought you were headed back to the good side," Bonnie said.

"Old habits die hard," he said. "But I repaid your kindness."

"How so?"

"I put it in a good word with the bosses," Eugene said. "They're interested enough that we're not just cutting you down where you stand."

"And I thought it was on account of the dishwasher I'm holding," Clyde said.

"Almost everyone is replaceable," Eugene said.

Bonnie whistled. "You're cold, Eugene. This job is changing you."

The kitchen door swung open. Percival Stubbs walked in. "Mr. Prentiss, please stop harassing the help."

Clyde released the dishwasher, and the man scurried behind big Lenny.

"And the knife, please."

Clyde dropped the blade to the floor.

"While I did not enjoy your little stunt during my dinner, I am mildly impressed with your rat-like tenacity," Stubbs said.

He studied them both closely, and Bonnie could see that he was coming to a life or death decision.

"You hillbilly types have odd ways," Stubbs said at last.

"They may be odd, but they could be uniquely useful in New York. Surprise your enemy, you know?" Bonnie said.

"All of this, the bank robbery and dinner stunt…" Stubbs let the question trail off.

"Think of it as a job application of sorts," Clyde said.

"A dangerous way to apply for a job," Stubbs said. He pulled out a cigar and clipped off the end, then lit it and puffed out a cloud of smoke.

Finally, after a minute that they both knew could end in a hail of gunfire, he reached a decision. "Have these two at my house in an hour. Unless they get up to any more mischief, then kill them."

Eugene nodded.

CHAPTER 18

Pointing fingers

A Negro maid in a starched, black uniform entered the room with a practiced neutral countenance. "They're ready for you, sir and ma'am," she said, her southern accent a welcome respite in the sea of urban fast-talkers.

"Where are you from, girl?" Bonnie asked, drawing close to the maid.

The woman kept her eyes down, but heard in Bonnie's voice the legacy of her own childhood. "West Dallas," she said.

"Well, now, that means we're practically family," Bonnie said. "What's your name?"

"Emma, ma'am," she said.

"Why, that's my momma's name," Bonnie said. The maid was silent, and kept her eyes locked on the floor.

Bonnie knew that a young woman in this situation was not likely to be trustful of overly-friendly white folks, no matter where they were from, and for good reason. She kept talking though, wanting to make a connection.

"May not seem like it on the surface of things, but something tells me our families have more in common than they've got apart, no matter what they look like on the outside," Bonnie said.

"And we've got a damn sight more in common with one another than with the folks you're working for,"

Clyde said. "Say, you wouldn't happen to be Sal's eyes on the inside, would you?"

"This way please," she said, ignoring both the question and commentary, as she led Bonnie and Clyde down a wood-paneled hallway.

Before the maid had a chance to knock and announce their arrival, the heavy door swung open and Angela Dunthorpe marched out. She stopped in front of Bonnie and looked her up and down.

"We took a vote. I lost," Dunthorpe said. "But remember this, I know your kind—white trash." She uttered the words as if describing, almost savoring, the most revolting thing in the world.

Bonnie coiled her fist. Nobody talked to a Parker like that, no matter how rich or pretty. She looked toward Clyde for permission, but he shook his head almost imperceptibly, and she reined in the anger. Now was not the time. "I doubt you know my kind at all," Bonnie said.

Dunthorpe seemed almost disappointed, never breaking eye contact with Bonnie. Clyde craned his head to look past Dunthorpe through the open door and saw Stubbs spin the dial on a safe and then swing a hinged painting—a ship sailing on stormy seas—back against the wall to hide it. Clyde tried to step back out of Stubbs's line of sight as he turned around but there was no room behind him. The maid stepped in front of Clyde, and he smiled, his eyes thanking her for helping block the view. The maid nodded slightly and Clyde wondered again if this woman was Sal's eyes on the inside.

Clyde strained to hear the conversation inside the room.

"Trustbuster, that's what he is," one of the voices said. "The forgotten man, my eye."

"We're forced to send a lesson, no matter how painful," said the other.

But then the men must have moved, because the words became muffled. Clyde thought he could make out the name Zangara in the mix, but wasn't sure.

"Say, may I have a cigarette?" Bonnie asked, keeping Dunthorpe's eyes focused on her. "I sure could use one."

Dunthorpe scoffed. "Beg somewhere else," she said. She turned and walked down the corridor, the click-clacking of her shiny black heels across the floor echoing the tirade of taunting names Bonnie screamed inside her head.

"Emma, release the hillbillies," a loud voice called from inside, and the room boomed with masculine laughter. The maid opened the door its full width, and Bonnie and Clyde stepped over the threshold.

A complicated glass chandelier hung down from the ceiling. Elaborate, gold-framed paintings of women in fancy gowns with large dogs and small children at their sides graced the walls. Double glass doors opened to a balcony with a filigreed iron balustrade.

Bonnie looked around at the splendor and wondered if there was any end to the riches and luxury of this new world she and Clyde had stumbled into. She thought back to the Hooverville. It was as if the people there and the people here lived on two entirely different planets.

Clyde cased the room quickly, noting the three strongmen standing alert against the walls. Men with biceps bigger than Clyde's thighs, and each holding a pump shotgun. A fourth shut the door and positioned himself in front of it. Other than jumping off the balcony, there was no way out.

Farquist sat on a leather couch sipping a tiny aperitif glass of port. He adjusted his spectacles at the sight of Bonnie and Clyde. Stubbs sat behind a wide mahogany desk under the hinged painting. He ignored them, sifting through a stack of papers and telegrams.

Clyde strutted to the middle of room like he owned it, a grin across his face. Bonnie felt a surging flash of pride, watching him bluster his way into this unknown world.

"Come on in, Brenda," he said. "Take a seat while us boys converse."

He pointed to the couch. Bonnie stepped forward, smiling, but then two of the thugs grabbed Clyde, forced him down to his knees and pressed a .38 to his temple. A third man pulled Bonnie from behind, holding her arms behind her back tightly.

"I don't like to mess with women too much, so I'll be mostly gentle, as long as you are," he whispered. She felt his hot breath close to her ear, and she tried to elbow him, but her arms were tucked snug inside his hold.

Stubbs raised his head to look at them, finally, and leaned back in the chair behind the desk. He put his hands behind his head and fanned his elbows out.

"What did you say your name was, boy?"

"Prentiss," Clyde said. "Clarence Prentiss."

"Well now, Mr. Prentiss and Brenda, we don't take kindly to people who steal from us."

One of the thugs punched Clyde in the face, while the other kept him down, drawing a string of curses from Clyde and streams of blood from his nose.

"What kind of lesson would I teach the den of thieves swarming around my city if I let you get away with this?"

The thug hit Clyde again, this time in the gut. Clyde heaved over.

"Cly…Clarence," Bonnie shouted.

"I told you already," Clyde said, grunting out the words. "Wanted your attention. No better way. To get it."

"Why me?"

"You're the man to work for," he said.

"Who told you that?"

"Heard your name in Texas," Clyde said, spitting out blood onto the polished wooden floor and regaining his composure. "From an anti-commie group. We came here for a new life, make some money, maybe have a few kicks, work for someone who wouldn't mind sticking it to a few commies in the process."

Stubbs was amused. "You hillbillies know something about politics?"

"We love this country, and we want to keep it ours," Clyde said.

"Your country?" Farquist said. "That's rich. It's our country. We just let you work here."

"Well, that's what we aim to do," Clyde said. "Work for you, I mean."

"You should see what's happening in Texas," Bonnie said, hoping she was adding something useful to Clyde's story. "No jobs, no food. We've got to steal to stay alive and fight to keep what's ours. And we've gotten pretty damn good at it."

"We could steal for you, and do other jobs as needed," Clyde said.

Stubbs paused and looked at Farquist, who nodded.

"This is your lucky day," he said. "We are willing to test you out with a job—of course, completely free of charge."

"Yes sir," Clyde said. "It would be our pleasure."

"Tomorrow," Stubbs said.

"Our schedule is wide open," Clyde said.

"Do you always work with women, Prentiss?" Farquist asked.

"Just this woman."

"Plus you will return what you stole," Stubbs said.

"Of course," Clyde said.

Stubbs looked down at his papers, then clipped the end off a cigar and lit it, studying the blade of the trimmer carefully.

"And one of you must pay a price for your transgressions," he said. "A permanent and visible price."

"I understand," Clyde said. "I'll pay that debt."

"Ear or finger?" Stubbs asked, holding out the cigar trimmer.

"No," Bonnie whispered, but the thug held her tighter, smelling the nape of her neck. She felt him getting hard against her leg.

"Finger," Clyde said. "Left hand."

Back at the hotel, Bonnie brought in a bucket of ice and carefully unwrapped the gauze from around Clyde's hand. Stubbs had cut the tip of his little finger off, and the blood was slow to coagulate. She guided his hand into the ice. Clyde winced. He took a slug from the whiskey bottle.

"Least they only took a bit of it," he said.

"Hold it in there to help with the swelling. The hotel is sending up the nurse to bandage it," she said. "You all right, Clyde? Maybe we should go to a hospital?"

"A little bit of finger is better than a whole lot of dead. It had to happen. And we can't risk questions at a hospital."

"You keep getting parts lopped off, and there's not going to be anything left." His feet were bare on the bed, and Bonnie glanced down at the old injury that to this day caused him to limp: the missing toes.

He was in pain. She could tell by the dull look in his eyes. "I'm going to take care of you. Don't worry," she said.

"I know, baby. Thanks," he said. He took another slug from the bottle.

"Clyde?"

"Yeah?"

"Where'd you come up with all that commie stuff?"

"It just came to me," he said.

"Any of it true?"

"I read some of those pamphlets along the way. Some of that stuff makes sense," he said.

"Like what?"

"Making things fairer, giving working people a voice," he said.

"It's a damn mess we're in, baby," she said. "I'm a little bit scared."

"I know," he said, wincing at the pain. "I don't mind admitting I'm a little bit scared too. But we can't let that show. Remember?"

"Yeah, this love we've got is fierce," Bonnie said. She kissed him on the forehead and ran her hand up his thigh, but pulled back at the sound of someone knocking at the door.

"That'll be the nurse," Bonnie said.

She opened the door, and Suicide Sal, a nurse's hat pinned into her hair and holding a medical bag, stood outside.

"Good evening, Mr. and Mrs. Prentiss," she said. "I understand you are in need of medical assistance."

CHAPTER 19

A hothouse full of smoke and memories

Royce eased the car into the driveway of Bonnie's house, walked to the porch and knocked. No answer. He rang the doorbell. Still no answer. The old woman's red Caddie was in the driveway though, so he peered into the window. The lights were on, but the house was still, the white porch swing creaking slowly back and forth in the wind.

The damn wind never stopped blowing in this part of Texas, he thought.

He walked around to the back and saw shadowy motion inside the greenhouse.

He pushed the door open into a humid jungle of orchids. A radio played Wayne Newton too loudly. Bonnie had her back to the door and was singing along, carefully misting a delicate flower striped with yellow and orange.

He cleared his throat and let the door bang close.

She spun around, pulling a double-barreled derringer out of her plant-apron pocket, cocked and aimed at his heart.

"Sweet Jesus, Royce, give an old woman a heart attack," she said, slipping the gun out of sight and then turning the radio down.

"Thanks for not shooting me," he said. "Sorry to drop

by unexpected. Hope you don't mind."

"Mind?" she asked, turning back to her floor. "Not one bit." She fussed with the plant a bit more and then returned it to the shelf. "But I wasn't expecting you until tomorrow."

"I found out something and wanted to ask you about it."

She put down the spray bottle and pulled off her patterned gloves and stood with her hand on her hip, facing him in a defiant pose reminiscent of an old-time photo he'd seen at the Historical Society. "Well, we're not getting any younger. Out with it."

"Why does the Grange own this house?"

She smiled and nodded. "You have been doing your research. The Grange network gave us safe houses on our missions."

"A farmer's collective provided safe houses?" he asked, the incredulity slipping through into his words.

"A fine bunch. Got us out of a pickle more than once."

Royce tried to call up what he knew about the Grange. His dad belonged to the local chapter and took Royce to a few meetings as a kid. All he remembered was old men playing dominoes and drinking sweetened iced tea.

"You'll understand how it worked as I keep telling you the whole story," she said. "But now that you're here, I got another piece of it I'm ready to share. Being out here with my flowers, missing Clyde something fierce, I got to thinking about how to help you understand all this."

"Yeah, what's that?" he asked. "More proof?"

"Of a sort. You writers are always talking about motivation—what makes real people and made-up people do what they do. Do you want to know what motivated Clyde?" she asked.

"Fighting the establishment? Escaping poverty?"

"Yes, that drove us both for sure, but there's more."

She looked at him closely. "I feel like I can trust you now. Is that stupid of me?"

"If you want the story to get out, and in the way you want to tell it, seems like you have to trust me," he said.

She turned the radio off. "Let's go sit on the porch so I can have one of your smokes. My orchids are delicate little things."

"I thought you quit."

"That menthol of yours tasted pretty good," she said.

"Are those pot plants?" he asked, pointing at a dozen or so bushy plants behind the orchids.

She nodded. "It helped with the pain of Clyde's cancer."

"Where'd you get the seeds?" Royce asked.

"The sixties was a wild decade. We met a lot of people," she said. She pulled out a drawer and raised a baggie full of dried marijuana leaves. "A little green with your whiskey?"

"I'll pass," Royce said.

He followed her to the porch, and once they were settled in, each holding a whiskey, they looked out over the flatlands as the sun dipped down, lighting up distant clouds, turning them blood red. She took a big sip and then started talking.

"Nearly fifty years ago, Clyde and I broke out two prisoners from Eastham Farm prison," Bonnie began. "It was the happiest day of his life. Mine too."

"I read about that," Royce said. "You killed a guard. It was the final straw. Got the federal government involved in bringing him and you down. That warden was furious."

"That guard deserved to die. Clyde finally got his revenge."

"Revenge?"

"It's a hard story to tell, but let me get it out," she said.

She lit a cigarette, and he noticed her hand shaking. He

wondered if she was sick. "Clyde was sent to Eastham with a fourteen-year sentence for car theft. One car. Not a bunch of cars. Fourteen years for one car. Everyone was stealing in those days. It was the only way to stay alive. He wasn't very good at it. Hell, no one was, but those are the breaks. He rolled the dice, and he lost, but that gave them no right to treat him—to treat anyone—the way they did. You know how bad it was in those days. You wrote about it."

"Yeah," Royce said. "Inhumane conditions, beatings, slave labor."

She shook her head, the memories clouding her mood two shades darker. "A man couldn't make a living off of cotton to begin with, but if you had prison slaves, you could turn a profit. A thin one, but enough. They worked the prisoners sunup to sundown in the cotton fields."

"Eastham had a god-awful reputation back then. Something like a third of the inmates died in those cells," Royce said. "They shut it down a long time ago."

"We were so angry after that, and that's what eventually led us to robbing and killing," she said.

"Not a very productive response," Royce said.

"That's true, but we didn't figure that out until after Sal took us in. Gave us a second chance," she said.

"So he was worked brutally hard in the prison?"

"Clyde was always a wiseacre," Bonnie said, smiling through the emotion. "Never knew when to keep quiet. And never knew how to back down. For such a little man, it was a bad combination."

"Especially in prison," Royce said.

She nodded and topped off her drink, then pulled out another cigarette from Royce's pack. He lit it for her. "Right off the bat, his mouth got him in trouble with the guards—he said something about their mothers or sisters—and they beat him down and sent him to the most dangerous cellblock, with the murderers and molesters."

The sun was almost down and night birds were swooping by.

"The prison had a system. They put the meanest, cruelest bastard inmate in each cellblock to keep the men in line. They called them trustees," she said. "As long as things were orderly, the real guards—the ones on the government's payroll—well, they didn't much care about how it got done."

She sighed. "Clyde's cellblock was run by a trustee, a brute of a man by the name of Duffy," she said.

"What did he do?" Royce asked.

"He raped him. When Clyde complained, the guards—the real ones—they laughed, and told him he probably liked it. Called him a homo and faggot. One time, a guard watched while Duffy raped him in the showers, getting his own satisfaction at the same time, if you know what I mean." Her voice had fallen to a whisper.

"The guard was…masturbating?" Royce asked, shocked.

"I told you the place was a hellhole. Him snitching to the guards just made Duffy meaner. He raped him over and over again. Clyde, my poor sweet Clyde, finally got his hands on a piece of lead pipe and cracked Duffy's head open in the shower and let him bleed out. The last thing he saw was Clyde's face spitting down on him."

"There's no record of Clyde killing anyone in prison," Royce said.

"My man was clever. He wasn't the only one had it in for Duffy. Some lifer begged Clyde to let him take the blame so he could up his own reputation inside the prison."

"Did that end Clyde's torture?"

"No," she said, shaking her head. "Clyde was so beaten down, so desperate to get himself transferred to another cellblock, away from the men who witnessed his shame, and that meant one where they didn't work in the fields."

She took a deep drag, and laughed as an old black cat poked its head out from under the porch.

"Moonie, do you miss your daddy?" she said. The cat hopped up by her and twined around her feet so she could scratch his ears.

"Clyde cut off two of his toes," she said.

"So he couldn't work? Good God," Royce said.

Moonie was purring hard, looking up at her with his one good eye and drooling a little from the pleasure.

"The saddest part is he should have waited," Bonnie said. "Not a week after he cut off his toes, they let him go."

"Why did they let him go?"

"His mother got him parole. She begged and begged the governor, and he finally relented. Probably all her pecan pies. Or maybe some other payment he demanded. Who knows. She never said."

"Jesus," he said, reaching for a smoke. The sudden motion spooked Moonie, who hopped back down off the porch and glared up at him. "I can see how that experience would motivate a man's choices."

"When I saw him after prison, I was shocked at how he had changed, but the electricity was still there," she said. "I knew life with him would be hard, but I wanted to stick by him. I wanted him to know that someone would be there for him no matter what—to love him and make him feel safe. And after I saw what it did to him, I wanted to burn down the system right alongside him."

"But you didn't burn the system. You robbed and killed innocent people," Royce said.

"Things might have turned out differently if they gave us a chance," she said. "From the minute he was released, the police hassled him every goddamn day. Followed him around. He couldn't hold a job, and pretty soon he got tired of trying. We decided to quit playing by their rules and just live free and plot the prison breakout." She shrugged. "And you know what happened after that. Things got out of hand."

"An understatement."

"He spent so many years running from those memories. That's why when Stubbs cut off his finger in New York, Clyde wasn't even all that upset. He'd already lost way more."

CHAPTER 20

Reports to file, wounds to bandage

At the sight of Sal, Clyde momentarily forgot about the grinding ache at the end of his clipped finger and considered putting a bullet in her. The source of their discomfort, unarmed—or at least under-armed—and alone, one slug could break their chains, he thought.

Bonnie, thinking along the same lines, sucked in her breath and stood up. She eyed the pistol on the table.

Nobody spoke.

Sal, ignoring the weight of their murderous stares, walked into the middle of the suite, placed the medical bag on the table, pushing aside a half-empty bottle of whiskey and another of gin. She picked up the pistol and tossed it onto the bed within easy reach of Bonnie.

Finger by finger, she pulled off a pair of gray satin gloves, taking her time, as the silence piled up around them. She took off the nurse's hat. A truck rumbled by on the street below.

The moment passed.

Exasperated by the tension and Sal's cool theatrics, Bonnie walked over to the table and reached past her for the gin. She grabbed a few cubes from the bucket where Clyde soaked his hand, the water pinked by his blood, dropped them into a glass, and poured herself a shot.

"Care for one?" she asked Sal, taking a lazy sip.

Sal crossed her arms against her chest, looking them both up and down, betraying nothing, her foot tapping in silent impatience.

"Are you pretending to be a nurse or are you actually going to patch up his finger?" Bonnie asked.

"I'll patch it up," she said. "But after."

"After what?" Clyde asked.

"Your report," she said.

"What report?"

Sal arched an eyebrow, and in the half-light of the room, Bonnie realized Sal was only a few years older—twenty-six or seven at the most. How had such a young woman come to be wielding so much power over them? Over anyone? So strange how things turn out, she thought, as other lives Bonnie might have lived flashed by—staying in Dallas and marrying a cowboy or an oil-man, moving to Hollywood, having some kids. Instead, she was drinking bloody gin while a spy or fake nurse or whatever she was, contemplated bandaging the severed finger of her man.

Bonnie roused herself.

"We got nothing," Bonnie said.

"Interesting," Sal said. "You robbed a bank, survived an assassination attempt, met the three industrialists in question, and one of you has a severed finger. And yet you have nothing to report?"

"Are you following us?" Clyde asked.

"You'll forgive me for not trusting a couple of murdering, joy-riding thieves who have already tried to run off once," Sal said.

She snapped open the case and pulled on a pair of rubber gloves. "We have eyes everywhere," Sal said. "Including in Dallas. Would you like me to report on what your families have been up to?" She emphasized the word report. "Well now, both your mommas are set on suing everyone left and right, apparently Blanche is writing a prison book, and souvenir hawkers are selling off pieces of your ruined, bloody car for a pretty penny. And it's not even your blood—or your car, for that matter."

"Everyone's making a buck except us," Clyde said.

"My momma is out of jail?"

"For now," Sal said.

"My sister too?"

Sal nodded as she unpacked gauze and tape and motioned for Clyde. He pulled his hand out of the ice bucket and unwound the bloody strip of fabric, letting the stub rest on the bed.

"That looks painful," Sal said. She cleaned the wound, the white end of bone winking in the half-light.

"It is," Clyde said, wincing. "How'd you get so good at doctoring?"

"I spent some time on a battlefield," Sal said, wrapping tape around the finger to hold the bandages in place.

"Why are you here?" Bonnie asked.

"Your report," Sal said. "I want to know what's next." She returned to the bag and rationed out some tape and bandages.

Clyde looked at the bandaged finger and held it up to the light, then nodded toward the whiskey.

Bonnie poured him a glassful of whiskey, neat, and refilled her own glass.

"We're running out of money, for one thing," Clyde said.

"And we need a place to go to ground," Bonnie said.

"What do you mean?" Sal asked. She pulled out a tube of ointment and put it next to the bandages.

"Things are about to heat up," Bonnie said. "We need

a hideout lined up."

"Tell me what's going on, and I'll decide if it's worth the expense of more money or additional safety precautions," Sal said.

"We got inside with the three assholes, and they gave us a job," Clyde said.

"What kind of job?"

"Don't know yet," he said. "They had to cut my finger off first."

"Just a little bit of it," Sal said, holding her fingers together. "You'll barely miss it. When does the job go down?"

"Tomorrow," Bonnie said.

"How will this help you find out who has been assigned to kill the president?"

"One step at a time, lady. One step at a time," Bonnie said. "We can't go any faster, or they'll know we're up to something."

Sal snapped the case shut. "Go much slower, and the president is at risk. It should go without saying, but if FDR dies, our deal is off. Not only will your family rot in prison, but we'll kill you."

"Just to keep things in perspective here, we've been in New York just shy of three nights and we're already on staff and just a mouse-whisker away from gaining their trust. That's damn good work in my book," Bonnie said, her voice rising.

Sal paused before responding.

"In the last four years, millions of families lost their farms," Sal said. "Those starving people you see in bread lines and soup kitchens? Those are the people who the banks and capitalists have kicked off their land, forced to move here just to eat. And that's not even counting the folks who lost good jobs. And they're all the lucky ones, still alive."

Bonnie noticed a split-second of pain flit through her eyes—a look that called to mind an image of a hawk's shadow crossing the prairie at sunset. She's got a personal stake in this, Bonnie thought.

"We don't need another lecture on how bad things are," Clyde said, his voice irritated.

"Yeah, we got that," Bonnie said. "But you never explained why these fat cats want him dead? What's their play? Someone else could come along after him and fix things too, right?"

"The New Deal is paid for by higher taxes on the rich. He's one of them, you know—American aristocracy, the elite, sons and daughters of the revolution, the original founding upper class. Now he's betrayed them."

"Trustbuster. That's what they meant," Clyde said, thinking back to the conversation he overheard outside Stubbs's office. "But that ain't enough to go full-hog gunning for the president."

"We suspect they, and maybe others, want things to get worse so they can buy abandoned land dirt cheap. When the economy starts to rebound, and it will, they will literally own America."

"Sons of bitches," Clyde said.

"That's why I'm pushing. There isn't much time. You must eliminate the assassin." She nodded at the medical supplies on the table. "The bandages are for Clarence. Change them twice a day. The ointment is for Brenda's leg."

"What about the money and the safe house?" Clyde said as Sal reached for the doorknob.

"Until I say otherwise, you can go to any Grange hall in the country. Tell them Sal sent you, and you'll be safe and fed," she said.

"What about money? We're running low," Clyde said.

"Check the medical bag." Sal walked into the hall and closed the door behind her.

Bonnie opened the bag. Inside were neat stacks of twenty-dollar bills. On top of the money was a grainy, black-and-white photo of her mother kneeling over Bonnie's headstone, tending scraggly daisies.

"Bitch," she whispered. Bonnie ripped the photo into tiny pieces. Clyde looked on, knowing that later she would regret her tantrum. Any photo of her mother was worth holding on to. He stood up, dragging the bedspread wrapped around his injured hand behind him. He sat down and began to count the money.

Outside in the corridor, Carl—now packing a shoulder-holstered gun—followed Sal to the elevator. "That was risky, going in there by yourself," he said.

Sal let out her breath, and leaned against the wall. "I needed to test their loyalty," she replied, relieved to still be alive. "It's holding—for now, at least. Come on, let's get back to Washington."

CHAPTER 21

All the world's a stage

Dan Rather read the nightly news headlines, his voice nearly drowned out by the treacle-smooth voice of Boy George singing about chameleons. Royce sat at the bar, thumbing through a stack of recent newspapers from around the country, knowing he should be catching up on national events and bylines, but his mind was stuck back in 1934. He sipped a Jack and Coke and considered his next steps.

He flipped open his notebook and looked over the scribbles from their last interview. Her description of the horrors of Eastham prison was rich with detail, as sickening as it was, and he wanted to keep it turning around fresh in his mind.

She sure could spin a yarn, but he still didn't have any rock-hard evidence to put before his editor. And he was already skating on thin ice.

In the last two weeks, he'd called in sick more than the entire previous decade. They knew him by name at the Dallas Historical Society, and although he'd made a dent in the mounds of papers and slides, he still had nothing tangible to show for it.

He had been to the two cemeteries and seen the headstones of both Bonnie and Clyde. Nothing but a bunch of graffiti and dead flowers and old beer bottles. Probably a romantic spot for rebellious teenagers, he thought.

The furniture store where the bodies had first been on display fifty years ago had been demolished long ago. Ownership of the funeral homes had changed hands a few times, and there was nobody still living who had memories of those days. There were a few photos on the walls in the mortuary where Bonnie's body had been laid out—a tasteful reminder of their brush with fame—but that was it.

He'd scoured every book in the library on the topic, including the one written by Clyde's sister-in-law, Blanche, and watched the old newsreels and a half-dozen movies, each one building out their own take on the legend of Bonnie and Clyde in ways that seemed more linked to the imagination of the writer than reality.

A young woman sat down on the bar stool next to Royce, interrupting his thoughts. She was dressed simply in Levis, a yellow T-shirt, and pale green cowboy boots. But her hair was teased high—dark locks piled up and braided into a coil around her head. And her eyes were elaborately made up; a lake of light blue shadow filled in the space between her eyebrows all the way down to her lashes, where it met up with a thick line of purple that jutted out past her eyes, giving her the appearance of an ebony cat. Ruby red lips completed the look.

"Hey, old man—buy me a drink?"

"You're late," Royce said.

"Rehearsal ran over," she said. She gave him a peck on the cheek. "And anyway, you've stood me up like three times lately. What's going on?"

"Nothing," he said. "Busy at work." He looked at her more closely. "You look like a TV preacher's wife. What the hell is going on with your face?"

"I look like a soon-to-be-very-famous stage actress

discovered at the community theater by a New York critic who just happened to be in Lubbock for his high school reunion," she said, taking a sip of his drink. "And I also look like I didn't have time to wash it off without being so late that I'd miss seeing my brother again."

The bartender turned off the jukebox and cranked up the volume on the news.

The Savings and Loan crisis continues to worsen. New documents revealed exclusively to CBS show that Michael Milken, otherwise known as the Junk-Bond King, accused of manipulating the market, earned nearly one billion dollars from Wall Street. Is your money at risk? Stay tuned.

"Fuckers," the bartender yelled, causing the slew of drinkers to stop talking and look his way. "My bank just put a withdrawal limit on my own money."

He looked around for commiseration.

"I hear you, Frank," a man at the far end of the bar said, finally. "Why can't these people earn money with actual work, like the rest of us?"

"You just got yourself a free drink," Frank said. "Hell, drinks on the house." A cheer went up as he started pulling beers.

"Why aren't you writing about that?" she asked Royce. "That's the hot story."

"Prison reform isn't interesting enough for you?"

"Royce, that was one article and a long time ago. Seems like it's mostly obituaries and high school sports these days," she said. "What's going on with you?"

He sighed and shook his head, nodding when Frank slid a free beer in front of him. "I'm working on something huge."

"A big break," she said. "Now where have I heard that

before? We're a real pair."

She took a sip of her free beer and then grimaced at the lipstick ring left behind. She pulled out a compact and looked at her face in the small mirror. "Yikes, playing a modern Texas Blanche really does require a ridiculous amount of makeup," she said. "I hardly look like myself."

"You look like a hooker," Royce said.

"I thought you said I look like a TV preacher's wife." She elbowed him and stood up. "Excuse me for a sec."

When she returned from the ladies' room, her face was scrubbed clean, and he recognized his kid sister again. What a change. And then he had a thought.

"Hey, do you think you could make yourself up well enough to fool Mom?"

"Fool her how?" his sister asked.

"So she wouldn't recognize you," Royce said.

"It'd be hard, but maybe from a distance," she said. "With some of those new plastics probably too, but I don't really know how."

"What plastics?"

"You know, like prosthetics or putty or wax like in that famous Madame Tussaud museum," she said. "Now come on, you promised to buy me a burger."

"Yeah, about that, I have to go. That thing I'm working on, I have to look for something. Rain check?"

He was already up and headed toward the door.

"It never rains here," she yelled after him, then looked at Frank and shook her head. "Any chance burgers are on the house too?"

Back at his apartment, Royce looked at the documents from the historical society piled up on the kitchen table. He'd paid more than he should have to get them Xeroxed so he could look through them at his leisure and without losing his day job.

Makeup, he thought. That could possibly be how the funeral was faked. But it seemed unlikely that kind of movie makeup magic was very advanced in the 1930s.

But maybe Bonnie's mother was in on the whole scam from the get-go. Mrs. Prentiss, or whoever the hell she was, had already sworn that was impossible, but had she been in the dark about that? Had Sal been smart enough to pay off the mother with so much money that she went along with the ruse? It would have been a way of saving her daughter's life. A possibility, he thought, but proving that was another thing entirely.

If true, it would break the old lady's heart to find that out now, he figured. But that wasn't his concern. This was a story. Emotion had no place in it. An image of her betrayed face, tears streaming down her ancient, wrinkled skin, popped into his head, but he pushed it away.

He kicked off his loafers and lay down on the unmade single bed, taking a box of the papers with him. A yellow cat jumped up on the bed. He nuzzled it behind the ears.

For the next three hours, Royce dug through piles of police reports, depositions, case memos from lawsuits, newspaper clippings, and looked at photos. He recoiled at the sight of the young Bonnie's face ripped to pieces by what had been a hail of bullets.

When he finally made his way into the third box, he found what he was looking for. Stuck at the bottom were a few pages of Xeroxed odds and ends—receipts and correspondence related to Bonnie's funeral and some faded telegrams.

Randy Masterson was the sender. The first one was to someone named Candy Masterson in Los Angeles. *Coming home tomorrow. Stop. Stick to plan. Stop. Buy steamer tickets today.* The next few were to the funeral home, detailing costs, but he couldn't tell what for. He sat bolt upright at the one dated the day before Bonnie's funeral. *No one closer than two feet to coffin. Stop. Maintain church temperature below 60 degrees. Stop.*

Royce picked up the telephone and called an old friend from his university days, now working at the *Los Angeles Times*.

"Still working the night beat, I see," Royce said.

"Waiting on the police scanner," Cal said.

"We sure as hell don't miss you in Texas," Royce said, meaning the opposite.

"Yeah, well, I sure as hell don't miss it, either," Cal said, meaning exactly that. "Not much international news is being made in Lubbock. But I'm guessing this is not a call from an old pal to chat. What's the favor?"

"Look up a name for me in the phone book?"

An hour later, Royce had called twelve Mastersons in Los Angeles and three in nearby Hollywood. The last one had said yes, her father was named Randy, and who wanted to know? Royce made an appointment to meet her the next day.

CHAPTER 22

The oldest profession

"How's the finger?" Stubbs asked.

"Hardly miss it," Clyde said.

"A small price to pay for a lucrative future together," Stubbs said.

"You mentioned you had a job?" Bonnie said.

Stubbs looked at her coldly and then turned to address Clyde. "Your woman forgets her place," he said.

Clyde smiled. "She didn't forget. We're a package deal. Now about that job?"

Stubbs opened a leather-bound journal on the desk, flipping through pages until he found what he was looking for, and ran a finger down lines of text, studying an entry.

"We find ourselves pestered by organized crime."

"Allegedly organized," Dunthorpe said.

"You want us to bring down the mob?" Clyde asked. "We're sure of ourselves, but that's a tall order."

"Not the entire mob—just one troublesome individual."

"I mean, okay, but killing a gangster seems like something anyone of your guys could do," Clyde said.

"A delicate situation," Farquist said. "One local cretin is sniffing around, using his brothel, the Saint George, as a means to blackmail some of our colleagues—men we rely on for certain, shall we say, intangible contributions behind the scenes at accounting firms and banks."

"We need to stop him, and we can't go at him head-on," Stubbs said.

"Your job is to neutralize him," Farquist said.

"A brothel and mobsters—a perfect job for Okie riff-raff," Dunthorpe said.

"We're from Texas, darling," Bonnie said.

"I'm sure there's a difference," Dunthorpe said, pretending to suppress a laugh.

"His name is Mignolia, and here's the address of the establishment," Stubbs said, scribbling on a piece of paper. "And it should go without saying—if you fail, we'll have you killed."

"Why do things that ought to go without saying always seem to get said?" Clyde asked, not waiting for an answer. "Just so we know the lay of the land—any cops have it out for him?"

"Several," Farquist said. "O'Brien, the district police chief, for example. He's quite the puritan, and there's nothing on him. He's straight as an arrow, with the perfect wife and brood to boot, but the mayor's office basically has a tab at the brothel, so he's never been able to make any headway shutting it down."

With that, Stubbs motioned for them to leave, and Bonnie and Clyde—escorted by a small army of well-armed thugs—backed out of the world of the rich and stumbled like paupers into the streets of New York.

Later that afternoon, they sat in their car outside the Saint George, a bar and converted hotel on the Lower East Side. Clyde ate Choward's violet mints. "Want one?" he asked.

She wrinkled her nose. "You've got such a keen sense of smell," she said. "I don't know how you put that flowery stuff in your mouth."

"I put you in my mouth, and you're pretty flowery," Clyde said.

She laughed. "How are we going to take care of this?" Bonnie asked.

"I got a plan," Clyde said.

"Is it like your last plan with the dynamite?"

"Better," he said. "Unless you got one?"

She shook her head. "I need more time to think through the angles."

"Time is the one thing we don't have," Clyde said. "That's why we need someone on the inside."

Her delicate shoulders fell. She felt the strap of the new satin camisole slip down awkwardly off her shoulder beneath the gray lacy blouse. She pulled it back into place. Bonnie suddenly longed for her old comfortable outlaw clothes, thinking they were better suited to these jobs than the fancy frocks they'd bought in Nashville. "Why do I think that's gonna be me?" Bonnie asked.

"Because whores are just like Hollywood starlets—real pretty and good at acting. And Bon, you're the prettiest of them all, and a good actress to boot." He flashed a bright, toothy smile at her. "We just have to get rid of the competition."

They watched the working girls walk into the alley behind the Saint George, getting ready for the night shift. A young blonde with short hair walked by and Clyde nodded.

"She'll do," he said.

They got out and followed her, and Bonnie caught her arm as she reached for the door. "Excuse me, darling, are you a whore here?"

"Not sure how that's any of your goddamned concern," the girl said. She looked no more than seventeen but in her scant years her face had already absorbed the worst life could dish out. Her eyes were hard as flint, her heart likely even harder, Bonnie thought, feeling a wave of pity.

"It's our concern on account of we have a deal for you," Bonnie said.

"Take a runner tonight," Clyde said. "We got one hundred dollars to convince you to hit the bricks." He held out a stack of bills.

The money was out of sight under her skirt in less than a heartbeat. "Consider me gone," she said, already pushing past them.

"Looks like there's an opening tonight," Clyde said, watching her leave. "Pretty little thing like you ought not to have any trouble getting hired on."

"Then what?" Bonnie asked.

"Trust me," he said. She shook her head in mock exasperation.

"Don't take too long," she said. "I'd hate to have to pitch woo with some old stuffed shirt because you were dillydallying."

"I'll be in directly, and I'll bust the teeth out of any man that even thinks about doing you wrong."

Bonnie smoothed her hair, still getting used to the way the locks ended just below her ears, and walked in through the back door.

In front of her was a long hallway with a door to the kitchen on the left, and on the right a staircase up to a second floor of rooms for the working girls. She walked down the hall toward the front of the bar, watching an older man with a girl on each arm head up the stairs. The girls were barely teens, and he was old enough to be their grandfather; he leered at Bonnie as they passed.

She walked through to a dining room that looked little different, except for a few cheap, decorative flourishes, from every worn-down sawdust saloon she'd drank in across the country, where men ate overcooked pot roast and boiled potatoes, and bought watered-down champagne for their dates. She walked up to the oily bar, and the bartender looked her up and down. "I think you might be lost, miss," he said. "This here's a...well, it's a, an um..."

"I know what it is," Bonnie said. "It's a whorehouse, and I'm a whore. I just got to town, and I heard this is a good place to work."

"You heard that, huh?" the bartender asked. "Who in the hell would tell you this is a good place to work? It's a damn hellhole."

"Lucky I'm not picky, then," she said. "Look, I need money and a place to sleep."

"You're a little older than most of our girls," he said, studying her closely.

"I'm only twenty-four," she said.

"Then you're a lot older."

He checked the logbook in front of him. "You might be in luck, though. Gretchen hasn't shown up. She's real popular, and you look kind of like her. Or her mother, anyway. Damn whores are a shiftless lot. Oldest profession, my ass. Nothing professional about you all."

"How's about you give me a try tonight," she said. "I can make up for my advanced age with a few things I picked up in Dallas."

"I hope that's things with your mouth," the bartender said. "Drill is the same for all the new girls. You got to blow the boss."

"No problem," she said. "Are you the boss?"

"Nope, but after that you got to blow me too," he said, without breaking a smile.

"Is that for real," Bonnie asked, "or did you just say

that because you think I'm pretty?"

"Does it matter?" the bartender asked.

"Not in the slightest," she said with a wink.

"The boss is in back. Name's Joe Mignolia. Hurry up and get us both off, and you can work a shift tonight."

"All right," she said, looking at the front door nervously.

"What's your name?"

"Brenda."

"Well, Brenda, get your ass on back there." He stopped wiping glasses and dropped the rag on the bar. "Or have I failed to explain the hiring process to your satisfaction?" He pulled out a baseball bat and tapped it in his palm. "Because there's other ways this night could end."

CHAPTER 23

Saint George versus two dragons

Bonnie eyed the rise and fall of the bat in the bartender's hand as the front door crashed open. Clyde had rumpled his clothing even worse than before and now reeked of gin. "I'm Captain O'Brien, and this here's a police raid!"

The bartender tensed and reached for the wall phone.

"Naw, I'm just pulling your leg," Clyde said. "Trying to get a rise out of you."

"That's the kind of rise that will get you shot," the bartender said. "What's the matter with you?"

"I've been on the run for too long now, courtesy of that cop son of a bitch, and before I settle scores, I need some company...of the female variety." Clyde pulled out the Texas accent hard, stretching his words into a taut, taffy-candy melody. Even after their short time in New York, he'd already noticed that the southern drawl tended to put people back on their heels, even if just for a minute.

"Take it easy, cowboy," the bouncer said, standing, trying to keep a grin off his face. "We've got an exclusive guest list here, and you ain't on it."

"I bet my friends are," Clyde said. "Grant and Franklin." He took out his wallet and pulled out some bills. "There's more where that came from if I can spend a few hours with a blonde spitfire."

The bouncer looked at the bartender. "Should we get Mr. Mignolia?"

"Is he packing?"

The bouncer patted Clyde's sides, his waist, and the small of his back. "He's clean."

"Doris, take the man upstairs," the bartender said.

A plump blonde leaning against the far end of the bar straightened up and tugged her dress down, accentuating deep cleavage. Clyde slipped his arm around her waist and smiled when he saw Bonnie stiffen.

"Doris, don't take this the wrong way, but you're too much woman for me." He slid a five-dollar bill onto the bar. "Here's a little something for me hurting your feelings. But me and my money have taken a shine to that pretty little thing," he said, pointing at Bonnie.

"She's new," the bartender said, putting his hand over the five-dollar bill.

"Ain't that something," Clyde said, taking her hand and leading her toward the stairs. "You always remember your first."

Bonnie glanced back at the bartender with a look of feigned helplessness.

"Room 214," he called after her.

Once inside, Bonnie locked the door.

"That was too damn close," she said. "Now what?"

"Now we see how good you are in the sack," he said, pushing her back onto the bed and slipping his hand under her blouse.

"Stop it, Clyde—I mean Clarence," she said. "Be serious."

"I'm as serious as a tombstone, Bon," he said, pushing her skirt up. "We got to sell this."

Ever since prison, Clyde took sex to a new extreme, like he was proving something to her, and himself, each time. This time—trying to make their activity known—

was even more pronounced, rattling the bed and banging against the wall until she almost fainted from the pleasure and the pain.

When they were done, she smoked a cigarette and watched him get dressed. "God, that was good," she said. "But I'm still asking, now what?"

"Be right back," he said. He slipped downstairs and bought a pint of whiskey, two glasses with Saint George coasters, and two turkey sandwiches.

He filled the glasses and slipped the empty bottle and the two coasters into his jacket pocket. "They think I got a score to settle with the goody-two-shoes cop O'Brien, so I tricked them into giving me his address," he whispered. "I'll be back as soon as I can. Make some noise once in a while so they think I'm still here."

He kissed her, opened the window, looked out into the shadows, and then turned around. "I love you, Bon."

"I love you, too," she mouthed from the bed. "Be sure to come back."

"I will. And don't drink all the hooch."

"I can't promise that," she whispered.

He disappeared outside. She stretched out and nibbled one of the sandwiches, then rattled the headboards for a bit and knocked over the water basin by the foot of the bed.

Two hours later, Clyde appeared at the window with a body over his shoulder. It was a young girl in her nightclothes, gagged, with her hands and feet tied.

"What the hell is this? Who is she?"

"That cop O'Brien's daughter," Clyde said grimly, laying her gently on the bed. "They've had enough of him. They're gonna turn her out. Get her hooked on drugs and turning tricks. Really show him. Now help me tie her to the bed."

The girl was shaking and trying to scream through the gag. She looked to be no more than thirteen. A splash of freckles dotted her terrified face.

"I don't know about this," Bonnie said. "She's young. Don't seem right. This'll ruin her, and she's a baby."

"No younger than you when you started," he said. "And you turned out pretty well. Mostly. Now come on, tie her down to the bed good."

Bonnie shot him a look of pure disgust. When they were finished, he said, "Let's go tell Mignolia that his newest girl is ready for business."

The girl's muffled screams caused her to choke and cough. She bucked against the restraints and tears streamed down her flushed cheeks.

Bonnie dragged Clyde out into the hall.

"Clyde Barrow, if you think I'm gonna let you ruin that poor girl just so we can get in good with the three barons, you've got another think coming," she said, hands on hips. "You've gone too far."

"Bon, trust me on this. We just need her to think her life is about to go to hell. I slipped her out of her house and left a couple of them coasters in her room, like maybe they'd been dropped. Now we're gonna call the cops and slip out the window before the fireworks start."

"That's actually a pretty good plan," she said.

"Did you think I'd whore out a child?"

"Your acting was so fine I was having doubts."

"Let's get this show started," he said.

He went downstairs with Bonnie on his heels. She sat at the bar, making small talk with the bartender while Clyde picked up the phone in the corridor, out of earshot.

"Operator, I need the police," he said. "Listen, I seen the chief's daughter bound and gagged at the Saint George," he said. "And she's in a real bad way. You'd better send everyone."

He hung up the phone and returned to the bar, catching Bonnie by the arm. "Come on, darling," he shouted, loud enough for everyone to hear. "Time for round three. Or is it four? Hell, I lost count."

The bartender shook his head and smiled. They raced back upstairs.

The girl looked at them, exhausted into a stunned and frightened submission when they threw the door open.

"Maybe I'll be your first," Clyde said, pulling the gag loose. The girl marshaled her vocal chords, and screamed. The sound shot through the building like a lost ship's foghorn.

"Yeah, scream," Bonnie said. "No one will hear you. No one heard me when I screamed."

But they could hear banging and shouts downstairs. "Time for us to scram," Clyde said.

They ducked out onto the fire escape and hit the pavement running.

CHAPTER 24

A small business loan

The three barons sat in the sunroom of Dunthorpe's mansion. Farquist had just cracked open a soft-boiled egg and was licking the yolk, like golden oil, from the back of a small silver spoon.

Dunthorpe alternated between sips of coffee and slow pulls on a cigarette in an ornate jade holder.

Stubbs dropped the newspaper, creased to box one particular article. He stabbed his finger at the headline. "Brothel closed in police raid," he said. "Joe Mignolia gunned down."

"How did you pull that off?" Farquist asked, dipping a toast point into the egg.

Bonnie and Clyde waited next to the table like attentive school children. Eugene guarded the door.

"Not so difficult," Clyde said. "Find the things people love most and use that against them."

"I bet against you, and I lost money," Dunthorpe said, tapping the end of her cigarette into a mosaic ashtray. "Quite a lot of money."

Farquist touched his vest pocket, and smiled.

"Lancing that carbuncle is worth it, I suppose," Dunthorpe said. "I admit—you proved resourceful. Or perhaps you simply have high native intelligence. Cunning, like cornered foxes."

"How you do flatter," Bonnie said. "Let's just agree that we got the job done and move on to what regular employment looks like. We're a little—what do they call it?—cash poor at the moment."

"I believe you're just poor poor," Farquist said. "Perhaps you should consider robbing another bank, but not one of ours. You have a limited number of fingers."

"Looking to get out of the bank-robbing business. Don't want the press thinking you've got another Bonnie and Clyde running around," Clyde said.

"As if you could enthrall a nation," Dunthorpe said.

Stubbs smeared thick strawberry jelly onto a scone. "Be at my office at noon. We'll set you up with an advance and a posting where you'll have the chance to continue proving your usefulness."

Eugene led them back out into the foyer, and without a word, closed the door behind them.

Out on the street, Bonnie looked at Clyde. "Momma always said it's not Christian to hate, but I think it might be okay to hate them. And that woman, most of all. When this is over, I expect me and her are going to have words."

"When this is all over, we're gonna burn their mansions down around their asses and turn them out into the streets to stand in a soup line," Clyde said. "But now let's get ourselves a breakfast big enough to feed a football team."

They found a nice place on Broadway and ordered too much, cutting wise at the expense of the three barons.

"Darling, you simply must try some of these eggs," Bonnie said, affecting a snooty accent. "Quail eggs are all the rage on the continent."

"Not for me, old pip," Clyde said. "I simply can't stop drinking this tea, fresh off the boat from China."

They dissolved into laughter.

After leaving the waitress a tip so big it made her check to make sure it wasn't a mistake, Bonnie carefully wrapped the remaining piece of toast in a napkin to save for later. Clyde asked for a scrap of foil, wrapped up the two leftover bacon strips and pocketed them.

They went for a walk, hand in hand, along the edge of Central Park and then hopped in a Hansom cab to take them to back to Stubbs's office. On the way, they leaned in close to plan, acting like any two young lovers while they talked.

"We have to get a better look at that ledger of his," Clyde said. "Likely has all their shady stuff in it."

"Won't be easy," Bonnie said. "Something that important he'll keep in the safe behind the painting."

"You saw that too," he said, nodding appreciatively.

"The side of the frame is polished from use. Only one reason you touch a painting more than once or twice." She bit her lip. "And you know as well as any man that busting into a safe isn't easy. Something tells me that Stubby didn't buy cheap. Not to mention the army of goons in there."

"Need you to make a distraction long enough for me to crack it."

She laughed, and not the pleasant kind. Clyde scowled, knowing what she was about to say.

"Clyde, I love you more than life. But you are not a yegg man."

"I could be," he mumbled. "I ain't never applied myself to the task."

"Now is not the ideal time to pick it up." She let her eyes drift skyward. "No, we need to take our own sweet time cracking that safe. We'll need to take it with us."

When they arrived, Eugene led them into the office.

Stubbs was alone, seated behind his desk, the painting in place and the book on the table in front of him.

"Thanks for seeing us again, Mr. Stubbs," Clyde said, removing his hat.

"What are we to do with our newest muscle, Eugene?" Stubbs asked, leaning back in his chair. "Should we trust them?"

Eugene, thinking back to when they could have killed him, nodded. "Trust, but verify, like you always say, Mr. Stubbs."

"Very good, Eugene," he said.

"It's not trust if you hold something back," Bonnie said.

"Girl, you are a hard-edged little harpy," Stubbs said. "Add a cigar and a Tommy gun, and you could be Bonnie Parker."

"Ha," Clyde said with a nervous snort. "We knew them two back in Texas. A couple of lazy good-for-nothings. We want a future, not a slab in the morgue and a hundred bullet holes in our heads. And I got an idea."

"This should be good," Stubbs said.

"I suspect the Saint George might be for sale at this point," Clyde said.

"A safe assumption," Stubbs said.

"How's about you buy it and let me and Bonnie run it?"

Bonnie's eyes narrowed at Clyde's slip.

"Are you having a laugh at my expense?" Stubbs asked. "We already established that you're no Bonnie and Clyde."

"I was joking," Clyde said with an uneasy laugh. "But I'm serious about the Saint George. You let me and Brenda run it, and we give you fifty percent of the take."

"Seventy," Stubbs said.

"We got to make some money."

"Seventy percent until you pay back the original investment, with interest, then we'll renegotiate."

"You kind of got us over a barrel," Clyde said.

"And I own the barrel," Stubbs said.

He flipped through his ledger to a mostly empty page, dipped his pen in the inkwell and jotted down a few notes. He held the book toward Eugene, who blew the ink dry, and then pulled out a stack of bills from the top drawer and handed the money to Clyde.

"It's done. Make this last until you start earning your keep. I'll tend to the deed. The Saint George will be ready for you by Monday. I expect to see money coming in by the following Monday."

"We are in a Depression," Clyde said.

"There are certain commodities, like sex, that transcend economic conditions," he said. "And don't disappoint me. It would be a fatal mistake. From here on out, limit your exposure. We find your manners appalling, your accents grating, and your appearance revolting. This is business now. Eugene, lucky chap, will be your contact until you both end up dead in the Hudson due, no doubt, to double-crossing someone slightly more duplicitous."

CHAPTER 25

On the run again

"Nobody talks to Clyde Barrow like that." He crouched behind a rose bush on the other side of the wide street by Stubbs's mansion, lit up for a fancy party and buzzing with activity.

"Or Clarence Prentiss," Bonnie said. She watched the well-to-do arriving in a fashionably late stream of overdressed and intoxicated excess.

"I mean it, Bon. That son of a bitch got on my fighting side."

She was used to his temper, lightning quick and too often deadly, and knew it would cloud his judgment for what was to come. She laid her hand on his arm. "Oh baby, like my momma always said, tea and revenge are best suited to a slow boil. He'll get his, but we need to get inside that safe first. We're not even sure we'll find what we're looking for in it."

"We will," Clyde said, flinging his toothpick angrily in the direction of the mansion. "Him and his kind, they're forever cribbing notes on who owes them what and by when. There's something in there, all right. But I don't know how we're going to get to it."

"When God shuts the front door, he leaves the back door unlocked," Bonnie said.

"How do you know what God says?"

"Momma took me to church a lot when I was a kid," she said. "Come on, I have a plan."

They slipped around back and watched the kitchen help and wait staff bustling in and out with racks of glasses, crates of champagne, sacks of produce, and slabs of meat. "This'll do just fine," Bonnie whispered, and motioned at a delivery truck with the tailgate down. The cargo bay was filled with fresh flower bouquets in tall vases.

Clyde dumped the water out of one, pulled a sawed-off, double-barreled shotgun out from under his coat and tucked it in among the orchids and roses in the vase. Bonnie picked up a second vase, and using the flowers to obscure their faces, they walked through the back door into the kitchen.

"I'm telling you for the last time, get those goddamned flowers out of my kitchen and into the main ballroom where they belong," the chef yelled.

"Right away, boss," Clyde murmured, and they headed inside. As soon as they cleared the kitchen, they took the stairs up to the office, retrieving the shotgun from the vase and ditching the flowers on a hall stand.

The door was locked, but Clyde lowered his shoulder and with two good shoves, popped it open. Once inside, he pushed the door closed and handed Bonnie the shotgun. "Watch for company while I open this safe and prove you wrong about my talent for this kind of work."

"Good luck, baby. I know you can do it," she said, thinking exactly the opposite.

Clyde swung out the painting that hid the safe, cracked his knuckles, and with a confident smile placed his ear to the cool metal next to the knob. With a furrowed brow, he listened carefully to the tumblers, keeping a light touch as he turned the dial slowly.

There was a click loud enough for Bonnie to hear, and

she held her breath expectantly.

"And that ought to just about do it," he said, turning the handle and jerking on it triumphantly. The safe door didn't budge.

"Hmm, it don't look nearly as open as I expected," Bonnie said.

"Just a minute, just a minute," he said. "I must have been turning it the wrong way."

He leaned in again and twirled the knob. "And open sesame," he said, this time a little less certain. He tugged at the handle again, and again the safe didn't budge.

"You are a terrible yegg man," she said.

"I never professed to be a yegg man," Clyde said. He sat down and tipped his hat back and glared at the safe. "Now what the hell are we supposed to do?"

Bonnie handed him the shotgun and reached into her purse and pulled out a stubby little stick of dynamite. "This was the other one in the box of goodies from Suicide Sal. Isn't it cute? Let's hope this one isn't a dud like its big brother."

He shook his head. "All along you didn't think I could break that thing open."

"Always good to have a backup plan," she said.

"Bon, you can't be going around with dynamite in your purse. It ain't stable."

"Clearly, I'm not put off by unstable things," she said, pausing just long enough for him to take her meaning. "But I haven't thought all the way through on how we keep from blowing the whole thing to smithereens. That's up to you. Dealer's choice."

Clyde rapped his knuckle on the safe. "It's solid as hell. But that little old stick ought to shake it loose from the wall so we can open it later." He looked around the room. "I'm going to tip this big old desk over to make

145

sure the explosion goes up and not out. It's a heavy monster though, so they'll hear me. You'd better stand by the door."

He tossed her the shotgun, and she caught it.

Clyde struggled to tip the heavy desk, which finally landed with a room-shaking thud. He smiled gleefully, like a misbehaving child, when the pens and papers scattered across the floor. Straining to move the monstrous piece of furniture, he pushed and pulled until the polished mahogany surface was flush with the wall.

"Someone's coming," Bonnie whispered and ducked out of sight.

The door banged open, and Eugene stepped in, a .38 revolver aimed at Clyde.

"Damn you, Prentiss," Eugene said. "The boss was right not to trust you."

"That's twice," Clyde said, trying not to laugh.

"Twice what?" Eugene asked.

"Twice that a skirt got the best of you," Bonnie said, pressing the shotgun into the back of his neck.

"Please don't kill me," Eugene said, dropping the gun.

"You are really terrible at this," Clyde said. "Last time, you told me if we let you live, you'd head on back to…where the hell are you from?"

"Cleveland," he said. "And that's where I'm going if you don't kill me. Tonight. I swear."

"Bonnie, what do you think we ought to do with him?"

"I like Eugene," she said. "He's funny. Maybe just cripple him? You know, shoot him in the knees or something. So he remembers us."

Eugene groaned. "Please don't shoot me. I learned my lesson this time. Back to Cleveland for Momma's little Eugene. I promise."

"I was just joshing you," Bonnie said.

"Here's the deal," Clyde said. "Get inside the closet and put your hands over your ears. You come out, Bonnie is gonna split you in two with this here scatter gun. You take your hands off your ears, and you're gonna be deaf when you get to Cleveland. Got it, sport?"

Eugene nodded, put his hands over his ears and stepped into the closet. Bonnie used a sash from the curtains to tie the handles shut.

"Get ready to light it," he said, pinching off half the fuse so it would burn faster. "This is gonna be loud, but not near as loud as directly." He pointed the shotgun at the wall and blasted a hole through the wood paneling just below the safe and above the edge of the displaced table. Bonnie lit the fuse, and he plucked the stick out of her hand, dropped it into the wall, and then pulled her out into the hall.

He reloaded the shotgun and then laid it on the floor, and they both scooted to the far end of the narrow passageway and crouched down with their hands over their ears.

Footsteps pounded up the stairs as a half-dozen armed guards appeared, standing on the landing outside the office, guns leveled.

"We got them," someone yelled. "Tell Mr. Stubbs not to worry. We got them. Don't interrupt the party."

Bonnie and Clyde looked at the men with guns and then each other. "I hope Sal didn't give us another dud..." Bonnie started to say, but then the world tilted sideways as an explosion leveled the office and the desk, but directed most of the blast up and into the bottom of the safe.

The force of it blew the room door off its hinges and scattered the guards like dry leaves, knocking some of them down the stairs and leaving others gaping like landed fish, their hands covering their ears, trying to tone down the percussive ringing.

Clyde was up and holding Bonnie's hand as they ran into the smoking wreckage of the office. The closet door had blown off its hinges and Eugene, scorched and smoking, his clothes shredded, was kneeling in shock with his hands still over his ears.

The explosion blew the safe from the wall like a cork from a bottle of champagne. It was upside down in the center of the shattered room. "Help me get it to the window," he said, and together they struggled it up onto the sill.

"Look out below," he yelled, and they shoved it over. The compact safe plummeted straight down onto the hood of a silver Cadillac with a sickening crunch of metal.

"Back through the kitchen," Bonnie yelled, and they ran past the guards. Shouts and oaths swelled from the ballroom, and they ducked out of sight into the kitchen.

The chef was standing in their way, a huge butcher knife in his hand.

"What in God's name?" he asked.

"One of them fancy gas lamps blew up," Clyde said. "You've got to get away from all these open flames. Get your people out of here."

They followed the chef and the press of people. The crowd poured into the back alley. Bonnie and Clyde raced to the side of the house where the safe was lying on top of the crushed car. They wrestled it into the back of another car parked next to it and jumped in.

"Stop them," a voice boomed from the window. It was Stubbs, and next to him the worried face of Farquist, and the pinched, almost relieved face of Dunthorpe—she had been right about them all along.

While Clyde struggled with the hotwire, someone

pulled out a Tommy gun, and bullets began stitching the side of the car and the concrete around them.

Bonnie opened the car door and fired both barrels of the shotgun, the pellets fanning out and ineffective at that range, but it was enough to cause the guards to duck. The car sputtered to life and with a whoop of triumph, Bonnie and Clyde sped off into the night.

"I may not be a safe-cracker, but there ain't a car made yet I couldn't get to turn over for me," he said.

Bonnie settled back into the seat and watched the headlights flare behind them as their pursuers gave chase. "Feels like old times," she said.

CHAPTER 26

Fame is fleeting

Thinking it was smarter to lay low that night to throw off Stubbs's men, Bonnie and Clyde decided to wait to leave the city until the full light of day. After a night of sleeping rough on the street, the safe hidden under a pile of clothes and scrap newspaper, Clyde stole another car, and they stopped by the Algonquin for their clothes and Sal's bag of tricks.

"Let's swing by the Empire State Building before we go," Bonnie said. "Oh please, Clyde. You promised."

"Baby, we can't take the time for that now," he said. "I swear I will take you there when we get all this nonsense behind us."

She turned her head away in a sulk as he pulled away, but then grabbed his arm. "Stop here, right this second."

He tromped on the brakes, earning a squeal of tires from the cars behind and a chorus of honks.

"What is it?" he asked, looking around for danger. All he saw was the New York Public Library building.

"We need something for the road. I'll be right back." She slipped out of the car and ran up the broad steps guarded by the stone lions.

Inside, she made a beeline for the shelves and located a copy of The National Grange for the Orders of the Patrons of Husbandry 1934 guidebook. What a mouthful, she thought.

She paged through it and found the list for the Grange halls of northeastern states. Bonnie looked around the library stacks for other patrons, but nobody was within earshot. She turned her back into the shelves and ripped the four pages from the guidebook, folded them neatly, stuffed them into her purse, and returned the now mangled book to its spot.

She felt worse about stealing from a library than she did robbing a bank.

Walking back toward the front entrance, she passed the periodicals reading room and saw a stack of newspapers and magazines. Curiosity killed the cat, she thought, but uncertainty was even worse.

She slipped into the hushed room and tried to make herself even smaller than she was. A few people hunched over the large wooden reading table, perusing recent newspapers from major cities. Circling the table, she saw none from Texas.

A young woman with glasses, her hair styled neatly and held in place by glittering bobby pins, smiled up at her from behind a reference desk.

"Excuse me, ma'am. Do you have newspapers from Texas?" Bonnie asked.

"Of course," the librarian said. "They're on the shelf against the back wall, but they are a few days behind, since they come by mail. May I help you find something in particular?"

"I'm interested in the Dallas papers and the coverage of the funerals of Bonnie and Clyde," Bonnie said, knowing she was taking a risk by asking.

"Such an event," the girl said, holding her hand to her throat. "Those two had half the country after them, and the other half hoping they'd get away."

"Which half were you?" Bonnie asked.

"It was all terribly exciting," the librarian said. She stood and straightened her skirt. "We still have many of the papers in the stacks since it was just a few days ago. Let me help you."

"No need, ma'am. I can find them myself," Bonnie said, imagining her picture in black and white triggering recognition from the librarian.

"It's no trouble," the woman said, coming out from behind the desk. Bonnie followed her to the bookshelves against the far wall. The librarian thumbed through a stack of *Dallas Times Herald* papers and pulled out several issues from the bottom.

"Here's the local coverage," she said. "But you'll find much more in the national and even international papers."

"Are you serious?"

"It was all the news for a while. I'll see what else I can find for you. Are you doing research?" asked the librarian.

"No ma'am. I'm just curious," Bonnie said.

The librarian left Bonnie with the papers, and Bonnie sat down at a reader's desk and switched on the light. She thumbed through the first three issues. Headlines about the death of the outlaws. Editorials saying good riddance and congratulating the police. Photos of her mother crying.

She read them closely, marveling at the difference between fact and fiction. She pulled out a few subsequent issues of the paper, but the Bonnie and Clyde story had been replaced by articles on the daring exploits of John Dillinger and Pretty Boy Floyd.

Bonnie startled as the librarian came up behind her.

"I found some more articles for you in other papers," she said, setting them down on the desk, and looking down at the photograph of Bonnie in her casket on the paper on the top of the pile.

"She was so pretty," the librarian said.

"You think so?" Bonnie asked, trying to avert her eyes.

"A real beauty. She should have been in the moving pictures. Too bad she got tangled up with that Clyde Barrow. He was handsome enough too, but a bad seed. They weren't even married." She lowered her voice. "My mother always says don't give a man like him your treasure until he gives you a ring." Then she smiled and winked.

"He's not such a bad seed," Bonnie said. "Wasn't, I mean." She opened the paper to a picture of them in happier days. "And he sure was handsome."

"You know, you look like her," the librarian said.

Bonnie froze and slowly closed the paper. "You think so?" she asked, standing.

"Sure, you could be sisters," she said, "But you're prettier. Maybe you should be in pictures."

"That's mighty kind of you." She looked at her watch. "Oh my goodness, where has the time gone?" she said, breezily. "I sure do appreciate all your help."

She grabbed her purse, leaving the librarian to wonder about her sudden departure. Bonnie pushed open the big doors and walked into the noise of the city. She looked around for Clyde and saw him leaning against the car parked down the street. He was fierce and still, watching her like a protective hawk. She rushed down the wide stone staircase.

He swept her up into his arms. "Bon, what took you so long?" he asked. "I was getting worried."

"I wanted to get us a list of Grange halls nearby— somewhere we can hide out and get into that safe," she said, sliding into the front passenger seat. He shut the passenger door behind her and hustled over to the driver's side.

"Good plan," he said.

Twenty minutes later they exited the Holland Tunnel, heading west.

"Seems like we just came through this tunnel the other way," Bonnie said, her nerves calmed.

"Damn, a lot has happened since then," Clyde said. "Where to now?"

Bonnie pulled the pages from the Grange hall listings from her purse and read through the list. She looked at the road map sprawled across her lap.

"There's a place in Lancaster County, Pennsylvania, about five hours or so from here," she said. "Looks rural, out of the way."

"Across state lines—that's always good," he said.

They drove in silence for a while. Bonnie ate one of the sandwiches Clyde had picked up from the deli while she was in the library. Clyde drank a beer.

"Clyde, I've been thinking," Bonnie said.

"Yeah?"

"You know we're not married."

"No, we ain't," he said.

"Maybe we should be."

"Don't it seem more exciting this way?" he asked.

"I'm serious, Clyde," she said, putting down the sandwich after only two bites and lighting a smoke. "It's improper."

He looked at her, realizing her mood was dark. "Bonnie, you're still married to Roy. It ain't legal for us to get married. Talk about improper."

She pursed her lips and tapped the door handle anxiously. "I was sixteen, Clyde. I was just a stupid kid."

"I'm not disagreeing with you on that. I'm just pointing out that you're still married, making it illegal for us to get married."

She cracked the window. "How do I know you aren't going to up and leave me?"

"Bonnie, I love you, and we talked about that in Dallas," Clyde said. "It ought to be pretty clear by now the only way I'll ever leave you is in a pine box."

She sighed. "That's what men say all the time, but what about when I get older?"

"I mean, maybe when you start to get ugly I'll leave you," he said. "But that's two, maybe three years from now, at least."

She socked him in the arm, and he pretended to be wounded, but then his voice took on a serious tone. "You're the one who's been married before. You're the one who had a boyfriend while I was in prison. How do I know you ain't gonna leave me?"

"Just drop it," she said. They drove along in strained silence. When they crossed the Pennsylvania state line, he pulled off to gas up, and they stood in the store and drank cups of sugary black coffee.

Back on the road, she started to get that sleepy look and scooted down in the seat to get comfortable.

"Clyde, I guess I married you in my heart the first time we ever robbed together," she said.

"Bonnie, you still thinking about that? You got to let it go," he said.

"I can't. We've been thrown into this situation. I can't really make head or tails of it, and now we've got to totally depend on each other, and only each other," Bonnie said, sitting up. "Forever."

"To me, that sounds better even than getting hitched," he said.

"I know, I just..." She put her hand on his arm. "I just feel something so, I don't know, almost unnatural for you, and I don't want to ever lose you."

They watched the farmland slip by—young corn and new hay blanketing the rolling hills. Well-kept farms, some barns painted bright red or decorated with elaborate hex signs, dotted the fields, next to abandoned land, laying fallow with boarded-up houses. They pulled onto Route 30 East.

"We are kind of married now," he said. "We are Mr. and Mrs. Prentiss. Guess that's one good thing to come out of this."

"That and we're not dead and buried with a hundred bullet holes through us and moldering in our graves," she said.

They looked at each other and shook their heads in disbelief. "Ain't life crazy?" he said.

CHAPTER 27

Shoo-fly

Clyde pulled into the little town and puzzled at the differences with Dallas—the bustle of commerce rather than the vacant buildings and the blasted faces of poverty; the green, bountiful fields instead of acres of arid dust; and the tidy, well-kept houses rather than abandoned shucking shacks.

"Wake up, Bon," he said. "Check this place out. It's like the Depression petered out before it even got here."

Bonnie blinked sleepily and looked around. "Wowee," she said. "The whole town looks like a fancy garden." She rolled the window down and took a deep breath of the fresh, cool air.

Clyde pulled the car into the parking lot of the Shillington Farmers Market. "Let's see if we can get directions to that Grange hall," he said. "And I need to get my hands on some tools or explosives if we're going to break into that safe."

A black buggy rolled up next to them. A bearded man in a dark suit pulled the reins, bringing the horse to a halt. A woman in a plain dress and white cap stepped out with a basket on each arm and walked into the market.

Bonnie and Clyde followed them into the simple, wood-frame building. Inside the market, six aisles were lined with stalls filled with produce, meat, milk, soap, and more. The smell of fresh baked goods was laced with the faint but lingering scent of manure.

The appearance of two strangers wearing fancy clothes turned the heads of the rural shoppers, farmers, and merchants.

"Maybe we better push on," Clyde said, instinctively unbuttoning his vest for quick access to his .45s. "We're drawing attention."

"We're not the only city folk here. They'll forget us soon enough," Bonnie said.

When he looked more closely, he saw the crowd included other people in suits and dresses. Bonnie was right. And the focus on them was short-lived, supplanted by the steady activity, banter, and exchanges taking place in the Amish market.

"We could always stay somewhere else tonight," Clyde said. "Maybe the back seat. We've had some fun there."

She shook her head. "I'd rather sleep in a big old featherbed tonight," she said, running her hand over a shiny pine one for sale.

"All them nights in the hotels have spoiled you already," Clyde said.

"Pardon us, please," said a woman in front of a small group of men and women.

Clyde tipped his hat, and both he and Bonnie moved back to let them pass. All the women in the group were dressed plainly—and nearly identically—in long, blue cotton dresses that reached to their ankles, sensible black shoes, and wide, spotless white aprons. The men wore black pants, white shirts, and vests, topped by wide-brimmed black hats.

"Did we drive so fast we went back in time?" Clyde whispered.

"I've seen some like them, called Mennonites, in

Texas," she said, watching the group pass. "It's a religious thing. They don't use anything modern."

Bonnie and Clyde walked down a row of stalls. In the waning hours of the weekly market, the crowds were beginning to thin, and bargains were being struck.

"How can there be so many different kinds of food for sale here?" Clyde asked.

The variety of jams and baked good and produce was almost overwhelming, and Clyde walked around amazed, his hands thrust in his pockets. It was a far cry from the farmland in the south, where the home gardens never made enough to feed a family, and everything else was given over to cotton or hay.

Bonnie walked up to a pie stand. "Clarence," she called, loud enough to jolt him out of his reflection. "Look at these pies! How much for one, darling?" she asked the Amish girl sitting on a wooden stool.

She was no more than eighteen, with fine blonde hair pinned up beneath a delicate white bonnet trimmed with lace, and soft, wide, blue eyes peering curiously at Bonnie. Though used to folks from the city, Bonnie cut an impressive figure in her sleek green satin driving suit and brightly painted lips.

"Twenty-five cents, miss," the girl said. "You are very pretty," she added, then blushed and looked down.

Bonnie beamed at her. "Why thank you, darling," she said. "And you are too—positively glowing." The young woman was pregnant, probably about five months along.

"You're kind to say that," the girl said, touching her belly. "We're sold out of apple, but we have plenty of shoo-fly."

"What the heck is shoo-fly?" Clyde asked, slipping his arm around Bonnie's waist.

The appearance of a handsome man brought on more

blushing. "It's a molasses crumb pie. A Dutch specialty."

"I assume it got its name on account of it's so delicious you have to shoo the flies away?"

The girl nodded. A man with a well-trimmed beard and wearing a bloody butcher's apron walked up behind the expectant mother. "We're ready to close. Dotter, add up your sales and red up the stall."

"I'll take two pies," Bonnie said.

Clyde balanced on one foot then the other, wiping sawdust and manure off the sides of his shoes with his handkerchief. Bonnie handed over a dollar, and the young woman made change. She gave the pies to Clyde. "Honey, can you take them out to the car? I've got a little more shopping to do."

They'd been partners in crime long enough that he knew when to take a cue, even if he didn't immediately understand why. Clyde took the pies and walked away.

"Now where am I going to find the best butter?" Bonnie asked.

"That will be my cousin Sven's stall, three down from here," the girl responded. "And you might want to try the apple butter. It's a local specialty."

"I don't mean to be rude, but what is this place?" Bonnie asked.

The girl's father peeled off his apron and stepped forward. "You are not from around here," he said.

"My husband and I are passing through," Bonnie said. "We're drawn to this beautiful part of the country. Tired of city life and all, you know?"

"We have a simple life here, but it's a good life," he said. "It is different than your wealthy city life."

"What makes you think we're wealthy?" Bonnie asked.

"Your fancy clothes, for one." He folded his wide arms across his barrel chest, unwilling to give even an inch to the thoughtless urban fools.

Bonnie looked at him curiously.

"I admit I am partial to nice clothes," she said. "But that will be changing soon enough in my condition," she said, touching her stomach lightly and shifting her stance to make it protrude a little.

He arched his eyebrows at her, but then softened.

"You are in a family way?" he asked.

"Yep, just like your daughter. It'll be our first, me and Clarence."

He let his arms drop to his sides. "A blessing, no matter the church where you find God."

"Thanks," she said. "And now will you tell me what this all about?"

"We are Pennsylvania Dutch. Some call us the Amish. Most of the stalls here sell goods produced on our farms," he said. "The English buy our products here."

"The English? That's a long boat ride."

He finally cracked and smiled a little. "No, you are the English."

"Are you like Mennonites?" Bonnie asked, watching as the girl began loading the remaining pies into a woven hamper for easy transport.

"They are not as strong in their beliefs," the man said.

"I am kinfolk on my mother's side by marriage to a Mennonite family," Bonnie lied. "I admire your dedication to a clean life and to God."

"The two are inseparable," he said. "My name is Ezekiel, and this is my daughter Abigail."

"I'm Brenda, Brenda Prentiss," Bonnie said. "Say, I'm looking for a friend of mine who lives on Doleniak Street near the Grange hall. Can you point me in that direction?"

"Doleniak Street?"

"Yes, Doleniak Street," she said. His tone made her fear there was a trap door beneath the question.

"The Grange hall burned down last year. There are no other buildings on that street. Do you have another address?"

"Oh, no," she said, crestfallen. "I must have copied down the wrong address. We were going to spend the night at my friend's house. Is there an inn or some other place nearby?"

"There is nothing. I'm sorry."

"I'm so tired," she said. "But I guess we'll keep driving."

"Poppa," the girl said, shooting him a look that was equal parts pleading and shaming. The man nodded.

"You will come have supper with us this night, and stay in our barn," he said.

"A barn?" Bonnie asked. "I mean, that's real Christian of you, but I don't want to sleep with the cows."

"There is a comfortable bed in the side room of the barn for English travelers. It is unused tonight."

Bonnie looked over at the entrance and saw two men in suits walk inside the market. She didn't recognize them, and judging by the bulges under their jackets, they were packing.

"That's kind of you," she said. "I do need to rest. You know the early months are tiring and precarious. Do you think we could go now? I feel a little faint."

Outside, after he put the pies in the car, Clyde walked behind the building. At the far end of the gravel lot, near a beat-up pickup truck and a rusting yellow tractor, a group of five men stood in a circle, laughing and passing around a bottle in a brown paper bag. Clyde walked up behind them.

"Room for anyone else in this game?" he asked.

"A nickel gets you in," said a boy not much out of his

teens, pockmarked with acne, as he threw the dice against the board. He rolled an eight.

"Damn," the boy said.

"Steep entrance fee," Clyde said, slapping two dollars on the overturned box.

Bonnie whistled from the side of the building. She was driving the car slowly, following a horse and buggy.

"What the hell?" Clyde said, jogging toward the car.

"Hey mister, you forgot your money," the boy shouted after him.

"Keep it," Clyde yelled over his shoulder. "I just crapped out."

CHAPTER 28

Supper and a safe-cracking

"Please pass me some more of the—what was that again?" Bonnie asked.

"Bot boi," Mariel said.

Mariel—Ezekiel's wife—was a small, stout woman with strong, rough hands and naturally rosy cheeks. Despite the fact that she was about to become a grandmother, she didn't look much past thirty-five to Bonnie. Guess the Amish like their mommas young, she thought, looking over at Abigail. Seeing them so content, and sitting at their bountiful table, gave her a strange twinge of envy.

"It's delicious," Bonnie said. "Like chicken noodle stew."

"Everything is delicious," Clyde said. He was amazed at the spread—hot potato salad, deviled eggs, green beans, pickled beets, fresh bread, and glasses of cool, sweet buttermilk to wash it down. "We're taking advantage of you."

"It is our pleasure," Mariel said. "Especially for you," she said to Bonnie. "You are eating for two now. You must keep your strength up."

"We're not used to this much food back home," Clyde said.

"Where is home?" Ezekiel asked.

"We're from Texas," Clyde said. "West Dallas. But my folks had a place out near Telico. Ever been to that neck of the woods?"

Abigail laughed lightly, and Mariel shushed her good-naturedly.

"It would be a very long buggy ride," Ezekiel said.

"Amen to that," Clyde said.

"What is raised in Texas?"

"Hogs, some cattle, but mostly cotton," Clyde said. "A few straggly old hens. The Depression hit us hard. Left the sharecroppers with nothing."

"This Depression is a bad thing for your people?"

"The worst thing," Clyde said. "People losing their farms, losing their tenancy. Grown men reduced to begging. Wives with nothing but the clothes on their backs. Ain't it hampered you none?"

"Fewer English with money to buy, but we grow for ourselves and our community first, and if there is enough left over, only then do we sell. So, if our labors are earnest, we want for little."

"I don't mean to be disrespectful," Bonnie said, "But why don't you want more than this? You have a nice home, but wouldn't you like some nice clothes, or a car, or maybe some books, or to go to a picture show?"

"We have everything we need," he said. "Faith, family, friendship, and food. Why would we put it all at risk by trying to amass money for things we don't need?"

"You make a pretty good point," Bonnie said.

"We don't judge others by their faith, or lack thereof," he said. "It's no business of ours, but to our way of thinking, money and false expectations, and the debt to the English that inevitably goes along with those things, erode happiness."

"And speaking of happiness, I have peach pie for

dessert," Mariel said.

Abigail served the pie. Clyde wolfed it down in four bites. Bonnie raised her eyebrows at him when he wiped his sleeve across his face, which he ignored, and then nodded when he leaned over to help himself to her slice. Six children of varying ages and height watched their every move.

Later, with the dishes cleared and the kids in bed, they stood on the porch. "Ezekiel, we're leaving in the morning," Clyde said. "Thank you for your hospitality." He pulled a twenty-dollar bill from his pocket. "I know you don't believe in money, but I want you to take this and sock it away somewhere."

"I cannot accept payment for hospitality offered freely," Ezekiel said, not really expecting this man to understand.

"It's not payment, and you will take it," Bonnie said. "If only so you have a little something in case your kids need it down the road."

"I will give it to the church," he said.

"You do whatever you think best," Clyde said, shaking his hand. "You're good people. America needs more people like you and less people like me."

"There is more to you than meets the eye, I think," Ezekiel said, shaking Clyde's hand.

"Amen to that," Bonnie said.

After the screen door banged shut, Bonnie slipped her arm into Clyde's, and they walked to the barn.

"I'm stuffed like a hog under an acorn tree," he said. "But we need to get into that safe and out of here before them barons track us down. I don't want nothing befalling these nice people on our account."

Ezekiel was already in bed, the candles trimmed, when the rhythmic sound of metal on metal began ringing out from the barn.

His wife looked up at him, startled. "What is that sound?"

"The English have curious ways," he said, pulling on his clothes. "I'll find out what they are up to."

"Be careful, husband," Mariel said. "Those two are strangers to the truth. That tiny woman is no more with child than you are."

He stroked his beard thoughtfully, nodded, and then clumped outside.

When Ezekiel opened the barn door, Clyde was naked to the waist, swinging a sledgehammer into the safe that bounced and jumped with every strike, but seemed little worse for wear. Bonnie sat on a pile of straw, the shotgun in easy reach, having a smoke.

"Evening old-timer," Clyde said, stopping in mid swing and leaning on the sledgehammer like a cane.

"You are thieves then?" he asked. "Common criminals?"

"Ain't nothing common about us," Clyde said.

"We're not bad people," Bonnie said.

"Are you even with child?"

Bonnie shook her head. "Nope."

"Why did you pretend?"

"Needed to get on your good side fast," she said.

"Then you are liars. And this safe makes it seem like you have stolen from others. What do you think bad people do, if not lie and steal?"

"We've done a lot of bad things in our life," Bonnie said. "A real lot. But this isn't one of them."

"If we don't get into that safe, something real bad is going to happen," Clyde said. "Something that could take this country down the wrong path."

"This country has already gone down the wrong path," Ezekiel said.

"Take those bad decisions and multiply them by like a thousand," Bonnie said.

"Why should I believe you?" Ezekiel asked.

"You shouldn't," Clyde said. "I don't care if you do or not. But we're telling the truth—we need to get into this safe. And we want to get out of your hair before anything bad comes of it. "

There was a long silence. "Look, this safe ain't gonna crack itself," Clyde said. "Do what you have to do—call the police, or get some of your pals with pitchforks— we're not gonna hurt you, you've been too kind to us. But I have to get back to it."

He started swinging again, the sledgehammer bouncing off the metal.

Ezekiel turned and walked off. A few minutes later he returned with another sledgehammer. Clyde smiled, and they began alternating blows, the rhythm and clang echoing through the quiet east Pennsylvania night.

Soon enough, it drew the attention of the entire family, who gathered around and watched silently as the two men sweated and struggled.

"Damn thing is stronger than the Devil's fist," Clyde murmured.

"The Devil is no match for a strong back and a pure heart," Ezekiel said.

"I guess one out of two ain't bad," Clyde said.

At last the metal around the hinge began to bulge and buckle.

"Praise be," Ezekiel said, turning to his oldest boy. "Son, go and hitch up the horse and bring him back with a plow chain—the stoutest one we have."

CHAPTER 29

Running with the greyhounds

Royce flapped his shirttails to try and dry the sweat-through—Los Angeles was a different kind of heat—before he knocked on the door. He stood in front of a small, ranch-style house, nestled at the end of a cheerful cul-de-sac, and waited for the bustling sounds to reach the door.

The old woman who opened it was not much younger than Bonnie. She had brown skin, deeply tanned from a lifetime in California, and an easy smile.

"Miss Masterson?"

"You must be Royce," she said, taking his hand in hers. "Please, call me Dottie. Could I interest you in a greyhound?"

"A greyhound?" he asked.

"Fresh grapefruit juice and a splash of vodka. I've got a tree in the back. A grapefruit tree, not a vodka tree." She laughed. "Although, wouldn't that be nice? I'm addicted."

"It's a little early in the day for vodka," he said.

"Pish-posh," she said. "Why is a Bloody Mary considered perfectly acceptable in the morning, but drink something that actually tastes good, and not like the ass end of a salad bar, and suddenly you're an alcoholic."

"You make a strong case," Royce said.

"I'll make a pitcher," Dottie said.

She showed him to the back porch in the shade, looking out over the greyhound tree, as well as a lemon-drop tree and two mimosa trees, and disappeared into the kitchen.

Dottie returned soon enough with an amber pitcher, studded with raised, decorative dots, and matching highball glasses. She filled his first, then hers, waiting politely for him to try it.

He took a sip while she watched eagerly. "Delicious," he said.

"We already agree on the important things," she said. "Now why don't you tell me why you're so interested in Dad?"

He hated this part of it. The truth would come out, of course, and he'd make his apologies later, but he couldn't risk leaking the story to anyone. Not yet.

"I'm researching an article about old Hollywood makeup and special effects artists. I think it might make a good book, maybe even a documentary film. Your dad, Randy, was considered one of the best."

"He was," Dottie said. "So talented. Give me just a minute."

She scooted into the other room. "I pulled this out after you called," she said, carrying in a large scrapbook.

The first photograph was of Randy, a candid shot from a backyard somewhere. He was tall and lean with a nose like a hawk—Royce saw the hint of it in her own nose. And he wore thin, round spectacles that made him look a little like a cartoon Bolshevik. He was in a light-colored T-shirt and looking down adoringly at a little girl, her hair a tangle of curls, who was reaching her arms up to him with five-year-old desperation.

Her old eyes misted a little, and she dabbed at them

with a pink handkerchief. "That was us in 1930."

She flipped through the pages, revealing carefully glued newspaper clippings and movie handbills. "This one was always his favorite," she said, pointing at one especially lurid miniature poster.

"*Seven Brides for Seven Corpses*," Royce said. "Sounds...interesting."

"It was terrible. Pure shit," Dottie said with a laugh. "He just enjoyed the challenge of making seven different monsters look scary in seven different ways."

She turned more pages and touched a fading newspaper clipping lightly. "He won a MUAH in 1948."

"A MUAH?" Royce asked.

"A 'Make Up Artist and Hairstylist' award. That's like an Oscar for a special-effects man. The movie was, *It Crawled from the Grave*. That was the very first movie that gal who got so famous later in the fifties and sixties."

"Kim Novak?" Royce asked.

"No, the one with the kind of bee-sting lips," Dottie said, pursing hers for emphasis.

"Anita Ekberg?"

"No, no." She was getting frustrated at herself. "More, um, bosomy."

"Barbara Eden?"

"Oh heavens, not that bosomy," she said, exasperated. "Her name escapes me." She poured another greyhound. "It'll come back to me. Or eventually I'll forget why I cared."

"So your father specialized in..."

"Corpses, yes," she said. "Vampires and the crawling dead, and even just bodies in funeral scenes. He was a real hoot around Halloween, that's for sure."

"How does one—I don't know—get that kind of skill for death scenes?"

"Easy," Dottie said. "His father—my grandfather—was an undertaker. Masterson's Mortuary. His first name was Morty, I kid you not. Used to be a big name around here."

"Morty's Mortuary?"

"I know," she said, laughing at the memory. "Like the setup for a bad joke. But Pops, bless him, didn't see a Masterson's and Son Mortuary in the future. He decided the movie screen was as close to death as he wanted."

"Pretty good logic, if you ask me," Royce said, jotting down the name in his reporter's notebook.

"Me too," Dottie said, dabbing at ice sweat trickling down the pitcher. "But Royce, I'm afraid I don't know the answer to the question you're waltzing around."

"What question is that?" Royce asked.

"Don't try to snow an old lady," she said. "There's only one question that matters: if he was so good, why'd he quit?"

"It does seem odd," Royce said. "He was earning a pretty good salary. He seemed to enjoy what he was doing, and he was winning awards."

"And then he just pitched it all and never worked again," Dottie said.

"Do you know what happened?"

"You're going to laugh," Dottie said. "And by laugh I mean not believe me, but I haven't the foggiest."

"Would you tell me what you do remember?" Royce asked.

"Of course," she said. "I'd love to see his name out there again. He was a big deal and such a kind father. I was pretty young, so I don't know the facts—just the events around the facts."

"Sometimes facts get in the way of the truth," Royce said.

"Well, it was about fifty years ago, around 1934 or

1935. I was nine or ten. We had been living in a little place on Las Palmas. Nothing special, but not a dump. It's still there. I can take you there if you'll drive," she said, refilling her glass. "Mom—her name was Candy—was an extra in a lot of the showgirl musicals in those days. No real talent, but nice legs and a great smile."

"And one she passed along," Royce said.

"How you do flatter," she said. "Anyway, things seemed pretty normal, and then one day we went on a surprise long vacation to London, and when we got back, we up and moved. Bought a big house up in the hills. I mean, a really big house. And Dad never worked again. Not in the movies, anyway. He tried his hand at writing science fiction novels, but none ever took off. Mom got real sick and passed away when I was twenty, and Dad took it hard. Got down in the cups and never came out. He died five years after Mom. Left me quite a bit of money, and I held on to the house for a while, but finally sold it to some movie star for a lot more money. I got married, got divorced, got married again, widowed, and next thing you know, I'm drinking at ten in the morning with a reporter from Texas."

She raised her glass, and he clinked his glass against it.

"You never figured out where he got the money for the house?" Royce asked. "Or why he never wanted to work again?"

She shook her head. "I used to think maybe he was a commie, and the studio paid him to go away, but seems more likely they would have just thrown him to the lions. And by the lions, I mean that dirtbag McCarthy."

"They would have."

"My first husband always thought he was gay and got paid off by some big-shot actor or producer to keep it quiet. My second husband thought maybe Mom got knocked up, and they paid her off to have an abortion."

"What do you think?" Royce asked.

"I think my first husband was an asshole, and my second husband was insecure. Mom and Dad were happy. He wasn't gay, and she wasn't sleeping around."

"Where'd the money come from?"

She shook her head. "I don't know. It's a mystery, and maybe you'll figure it out. Make that book you want to write spicy enough to sell."

"Do you mind if I keep poking around a little?"

"Why would I care?" she asked.

"You may not like what I find out."

"Unless it somehow results in my trees getting cut down, I doubt there's anything that could cause me much grief these days. I'm going to make us a little snack—something to soak up the vodka—but in the meantime, you might want to write down the name Abe Schenkel. He was kind of like an apprentice to Dad back before he quit. We stay in touch—Christmas cards and such. He's an old man now, retired, but he stayed in the business for a lot of years. Lives up in Loma Linda, maybe."

CHAPTER 30

Dirty pictures, moral failings, and high fashion

After a sunrise breakfast of biscuits and gravy, eggs over easy, thick slices of grilled ham, and griddle cakes, Bonnie and Clyde left Ezekiel and his family behind.

"One more meal with them folks, and I wouldn't have fit into my pants," Clyde said.

They drove south through the gentle hills of rural Pennsylvania on back county roads. Bonnie put on her dark sunglasses, and Clyde pulled his fedora low over his eyes.

"Still can't quite figure why those people were so kind to us," Bonnie said. "They treated us like family."

"Hell, they treated us better than family," Clyde said. "And probably because I'm so handsome."

She gave him a lazy, back-handed swat. "More likely, it was on account of how smart I am."

"And beautiful too," Clyde said. "But all that matters is we got what we needed."

"I guess so," Bonnie said, but she kept turning the question over in her mind. If she was honest, and the roles were reversed, she probably would have booted them out in the middle of the night, and maybe even stolen their money too. "Even after they found out we were lying about being pregnant, they still helped us. What makes people good like that?"

"Kind or stupid—not sure there's much difference,"

Clyde said. "Not in this world, anyways."

"That's harsh," she said. She cracked the window.

"Life is harsh," he said. "That's why when you got a good thing, you hold on to it. You know, I got an idea why they was so nice."

"Yeah, why's that?" she asked, shaking out a cigarette.

"When they found out you wasn't pregnant, they was probably so damn relieved to know that the likes of us weren't procreating, filling the world with English devil offspring," he said. "The joy practically spilled out of them."

She laughed and lit her cigarette. "If we did have a baby, it would probably pop out with a Tommy gun in his little fingers," she said, exhaling out the cracked top of the window.

He slapped his thigh and let out a loud chuckle. "First words out of her mouth would probably be a string of curses."

"Followed by a lie," she said, laughing harder, covering her mouth.

"If it was a boy, he'd probably shit bullets," Clyde said.

"If it was a girl, she'd probably be born smoking a cigarette," she said.

They were laughing so much they nearly missed the turnoff, but Bonnie saw the sign and pointed. "Turn here, here," she shouted.

He cranked the wheel so hard that the Ford slid and screeched into the turn. The jolt caused her to scream, as she flashed back to the car accident at the bridge and the leg burns. He braked and took her hand.

"Bon, I'm sorry."

She was shaking. The sudden jerk spilled the contents of the burlap bag that seconds before had been between them out across her lap.

"I'll slow down. Meanwhile, why don't you take a look at what was in that safe," he said, mostly hoping to distract her from the fright.

Last night, after Ezekiel helped Clyde pry open the battered safe, he made clear he wanted nothing to do with the materials inside. Didn't even want to know what they were. Bonnie stuffed them quickly into a burlap bag, and Clyde tossed the remnants of the safe, what little was left, into the car's trunk. The risk of a light in the barn, in a world where sundown meant darkness, seemed too great, so they decided to wait until daytime and put distance between them and the farm.

Bonnie began sorting through the mess strewn across the front seat, ordering the papers as she examined them.

There was the detailed ledger—page after page, column after column of names, numbers, dollar signs, and cryptic notes that went back years.

There were contracts between Stubbs and vendors, companies providing services, a dozen or more papers related to employees, and stacks of real estate deeds.

There was a packet of receipts for services rendered and goods bought.

There were two sealed envelopes.

And there was a map colored in blue, yellow, and red. Bonnie studied it. "Seems to be a map of New York City," she said. She looked more carefully. She read the fine print in the legend at the edge of the document. "Kinda hard to make out but I think this is a banker's map, showing where it's okay to loan money and where it's not."

"What's the difference in the colors?" Clyde asked, looking away from the road for a second at the map spread out on Bonnie's lap.

"As far as I can tell, seems like the red-lined areas are

where the government says not to back any mortgages," she said.

"Who lives there?"

"I'm not all that familiar with the city, but it's sure not the rich side of town," she said.

"Probably the place where the likes of us would live, right alongside the black folk," he said.

She folded up the map. "If I understand this, seems like this New Deal stuff isn't all for the working man," she said. "Looks like they're helping bankers divide up spoils too."

"Why wouldn't they want to loan money in the red areas? As long as they can pay it back, who cares?"

"Some money is better than other money, and some folks are more desirable neighbors than others," she said.

Bonnie stuffed the map back into the sack and then looked long and hard at Clyde.

"What?" he asked. "What is it?"

"Clyde, you know, there isn't any such thing as good guys in white hats," she said. "Even that president of ours, the one we're supposed to be saving—all of them. They'd get rid of the likes of us if they could."

"I reckon, yeah," he said.

"They need us to believe some fairy tale that we can improve our lot if we just work hard enough and save careful enough," Bonnie said. "But we can't—not when everything is stacked against us. Not the way things are."

"It's sort of like a big game of craps," Clyde said.

"I don't follow," she said.

"A few folks win at craps, and they take home a bundle of cash, but the rest of the players just keep forking money over, thinking their luck will turn," Clyde said. "And the ones running the game, they keep pointing at the winners as proof that anyone can win, so that all the players keep on throwing their cash into the pot to feed that fantasy. But half the time, them same ones running the game are letting their friends win with loaded dice while the rest of us just keep thinking someday it's gotta be our turn."

"And then the ones running the game tell us it's our own damn fault for not winning because they gave us a chance to play the game in the first place," Bonnie said.

He nodded. "I'm starting to appreciate the complexities of Sal's world. And as odd as it may sound, I think we've got a chance here to do more good than bad for once."

"I hope you're right," Bonnie said.

"Don't see much choice in the matter for now," he said.

Bonnie picked up the two sealed envelopes, one marked with an F, the other with a D. She opened the larger of the two, the one marked D, and three photos dropped out—nude photos of Angela Dunthorpe in a passionate embrace.

"Holy moley," Clyde said, adding a wolf whistle. "She's naked as a jaybird."

"Down boy," Bonnie said, holding up the black and white photos. "Looks like Miss Dunthorpe has a secret."

"She ain't being very secretive in those photos," Clyde said, switching his attention from the road to the pictures and back again.

"She has a lovely figure, that's for sure," Bonnie said.

"She ain't a natural blonde, that's also for sure," he said.

"Don't be crude," Bonnie said. "Who do you suppose that is with her?"

"And by with her, you mean in her?"

"Seriously Clyde, treat me like a lady occasionally," Bonnie said. "Hard to tell if she knew these photos were being taken or not. But we can safely assume that it's not someone she's supposed to be with."

"Blackmail?"

"He looks familiar, but I can't quite place him. Let's see what F shows us." She opened the other envelope and pulled out an official-looking letter.

When it wasn't more naked pictures, Clyde returned his gaze to the road.

Bonnie scanned it quickly. "It seems our elegant Mr. Farquist has a thing for little boys," she said.

Clyde gripped the steering wheel tightly and clenched his teeth. "I'm gonna go back and kill him," he said.

"This is a notarized letter provided to Stubbs's lawyer by a boy's mother," Bonnie said.

"Why not the police?"

"Money, I suppose," she said. "Looks like he has something on both of them."

"Why blackmail your partners?" Clyde asked.

"Didn't you learn anything from our days running the Barrow gang? There's always intrigues and maneuvering going on whenever people are involved," she said. "Doesn't matter if it's for a little money or a lot of money. It's human nature. He was probably keeping these secret for when he needed extra leverage."

Bonnie slid the photos and letter back into the envelopes. "None of this helps us much with the assassin," she said.

A road sign showed they were about to drive through the town of Reading. "I know how that big brain of your works," Clyde said. "You let all them facts rattle around in there while we see the sights and have us a fancy lunch. Then maybe later an answer will pop out."

He turned the car off the county road, and they drove down into Reading and then on up Mt. Penn on the far side of the town to the Reading Pagoda. They parked and walked around the site, reading the signs about the history of the culturally misplaced monument.

"Isn't that something," Bonnie said. "Some big shot built a Japanese hotel to cover up his defunct quarry."

They drove back down toward town, but Bonnie asked him to meander through the residential neighborhoods. He groaned, but only in his head. During their time running, she had picked up the habit of looking at houses, dreaming about where they would land some day, and what life inside their own house would be like.

"That's a pretty one," Bonnie said, pointing to a Victorian-style mansion behind a tall hedge. "I wonder who lives there." Her attention flitted to a white colonial with the wrap-around columned front porch on the other side of the street. A woman in a starched white uniform pushed a pram on the sidewalk.

"We stumbled into the rich neighborhood," Clyde said.

"I love looking at these fancy houses, and thinking about the lives of the people who live here. Do you think they are all happy? Anyone living here must be happy, right?"

"I don't know," he said. "I've never owned a house, and I reckon as long as I'm with you, I'm happier than any rich man."

She patted his hand, but she was lost in the immaculate balconies, scented lilac gardens, and copper-plated turrets. Clyde dutifully nodded each time she praised some particular feature until she'd dreamed her fill and motioned for him to go downtown.

"Think someday we could have a house?" she said, as they headed down the hill.

"If you'd asked me a few weeks ago, I'd have said no," he said. "Now I think maybe the odds are seventy-thirty."

"I want a brick house. They seem strong and like

they'd last forever. What about you, Clyde?"

"Brick will be just fine," he said, thinking what a terrible and misplaced life he'd given her. "As long as it ain't in Texas."

He parked near the Abe Lincoln Hotel, and they ate lunch in the dining room—baked chicken and red potatoes, with an ice cream sundae for dessert.

As they left the town, they crossed the train tracks and drove past wooden row houses built nearly on top of one another. Barefoot children played in the street with empty cans. The air was heavy with coal soot. Minutes later, they were back on the county road, and she was digging through the sack of papers again.

"You had an idea, didn't you?" he asked.

"I realized there wouldn't be anything obvious about paying an assassin," she said, thumbing through the contracts. "I want to look for something that stands out from all the rest."

She flipped through the papers again, more slowly this time, then stopped and thumbed backward. "Is Stubbs married?" Bonnie asked.

"Who'd marry that stuffed shirt?"

"With that kind of money, half the women in Texas," Bonnie said. "This is odd," she said, pulling out a contract. "This one is for services rendered from a dressmaker in Washington, DC. And I know the name. She designs gowns for big movie stars. Why would Stubbs have a contract with her?"

She pulled out the notebook ledger and thumbed through the pages, tracing the column with dates until she found something, then sliding her finger to the dollar amount. She whistled.

"What is it?"

"He just made a big payment to the dressmaker," she

said.

"To a dressmaker in Washington, DC," Clyde said. "Where the president lives."

"And goes to fancy parties," Bonnie said. "We need to call Sal." She looked at the map and the ripped pages of Grange addresses. "Pottsville is north of here. There's a Grange hall there."

"Shit," Clyde said, looking in the rearview mirror at a gray car coming up fast behind them. "It's gonna be a rough ride. We've been made."

CHAPTER 31

Road rage

Clyde craned his neck to look behind them at the car bearing down, a new gray touring sedan. He tipped his hat up to see more of the road and grabbed the wheel with both hands.

"Hang on, Bon, this is about to get exciting," he said, tromping on the gas. "And for you, a little terrifying."

"Do what you have to do, Clyde," she said, pulling out a .45, chambering a round, and then clutching the door handle in a death grip with her free hand.

The car was gaining on them. "They got more horsepower than we do, but not more firepower. I'm gonna do a Tulsa Turnaround, so brace yourself."

He stomped on the brakes, cranked the wheel and pulled the parking brake, sending the car into a tight, squealing, sliding turn. As it flipped around, he let off the brake and gave it some gas, and suddenly they were heading right back at their pursuers.

"I'll be damned. Is that Eugene?" Clyde asked, taking the gun from Bonnie's hand and firing seven shots into the engine and windshield as they passed the car. The men inside, their face doughy shadows, ducked as the slugs whistled past.

The pursuing car ground to a halt in a whoosh of steam from the punctured engine. Clyde roared past and then slammed on the brakes and turned the wheel sharp to the left, so they slid to a stop. "Give 'em hell, honey," he said.

Bonnie snatched a BAR from the back seat and stepped out onto the highway and sprayed the back of the car with bullets. A rain of heavy slugs shattered the glass and punched holes through the steel. The doors flew open, and four men scrambled out, one clutching his shoulder with blood seeping between his fingers. Another limped as they dove for cover in the leaf-choked ditches beside the road.

One of the four didn't bother to stay hidden; instead he was loping with a peculiar, shuffling gate toward some nearby trees.

"Still going to Cleveland," Clyde said, grinning.

Bonnie slapped in a fresh clip and aimed at Eugene's retreating form, sending fifteen rounds in his direction but above his head. "You'd better add a little mustard to that run, Eugene," she yelled, laughing as he reached the trees and disappeared from sight.

They hopped back in their car, turned around and sped past the abandoned vehicle. One of the men struggled up out of the ditch to shoot at them, the puffs of smoke from his revolver visible in the cool evening air, but he only managed to hit the back window twice.

"Something tells me they're probably not the only ones looking for us," Clyde said, driving away at a breakneck speed. "We'd best be real careful."

A few miles later, it seemed like they had lost their pursuers. They approached a filling station, and Clyde slowed. "Let's fill up, and take some gas with us so we don't have to stop later."

The filling station attendant, a handsome teenager with dark hair and a floppy hat, filled up the tank and the gas can they bought, wrapped up some roast beef sandwiches his mother sold for a nickel apiece, and then cleaned the windows with his best rag.

"Uh, folks, you got a little, well, you've got a couple holes in the back window glass," he said. "Looks like you been shot at?"

"No, no," Clyde said laughing. "It's my nephew. That scamp has a slingshot. Boy, when I get home I'm going to tan his hide."

"He must have one heck of a slingshot," the boy said. "Because he put one right through the metal too."

Clyde reached for his gun but Bonnie stopped him. "What's your name?"

"Warren."

"Warren, we got into a little scrape with some big city types. Bankers. They're on our tail, and we need to be on our way without arousing attention."

"Bankers, you say?" Warren asked.

"That's right."

"Never had much use for bankers. You get on your way, and if anybody comes a-looking, I'll point them the other direction."

"Much appreciated," Bonnie said.

"Slingshot my eye," he muttered, walking back inside.

As they continued through farm country and fields of green and amber, tractors putting through barnyards, old dogs sleeping on porches, and kids waving as the car passed, they felt like they just might make it out of the scrape unscathed.

In the sun and bucolic scenery, lulled by the rocking of the car, Bonnie started getting road sleepy, her eyelids shutting for longer and longer periods, her head bobbing, until soon enough she was sleeping.

Clyde kept looking over, struck by how peaceful she

looked, like an angel, until he topped the crest of a long hill and almost ran straight into a roadblock.

A dozen cars, some of them with police markings, blocked the narrow county road. They were fanned out and angled together, so smashing through them was not an option. And behind them, men armed with shotguns and machine guns glared at the approaching car.

Clyde snarled and slammed on the brakes. "Looks like them three barons bought up the local police department."

Bonnie, startled awake, looked at the barrier in dismay. "It doesn't ever end."

Clyde put the car in reverse, even as shouting and shots rang out from the barricade. Behind them, more cars were racing up the highway, boxing them in. "We're not going down like this," Clyde said, stepping on the accelerator and guiding the car off the road, through a rickety fence, and into a recently plowed field.

Three cars pursued them as they raced down the hill, and the others stayed at the top, the drivers and passengers firing their weapons down at the speeding car. Bullets kicked up geysers of soil near the car, and occasionally one smacked into the roof.

The field was rough but passable, and Clyde aimed the car for a rickety bridge crossing a muddy stream at the bottom.

"I don't like the looks of that bridge," Bonnie said, bracing herself against the door.

"It'll hold," he said, hopefully. "Trust me."

The bridge mostly held, shaking into splinters on the left side as their car bounced over it. With a roar of triumph, they rocketed up the other side. The closest car behind was not so lucky, hitting the sagging left side with its front tire, cratering the whole thing to kindling, and planting the car in the muddy water with a thud.

The cars on the crest of this hill took to the highway and began racing toward the driveway up to the farm below.

"Sorry," Bonnie yelled as their car plowed through the front yard of the farmhouse and snagged the clothesline. A woman shrieked, dropped her basket of laundry, and raced for the safety of the house as the car sped past, dragging the line of now-soiled clothes behind them.

Clyde accelerated through the barnyard, sending squawking chickens every which way. The farmer fired an old shotgun into the air, yelling for them to stop tearing everything up, but Clyde sped past and waved.

"Even if we make it to the highway, this poor old car is about used up," he said.

"Then we best find another," Bonnie said.

"You got an idea?" he asked.

"Let them catch us and we take one of their cars. That old barn over there should be perfect. Road's too narrow for all them cars. They'll have to come in one at a time and end up boxing themselves in."

He pulled onto the highway and then turned immediately onto an old dirt road leading to a dilapidated barn with a windmill on one side and a stack of golden hay on the other.

They rolled right into the barn, and Clyde jumped out to slam the door shut behind them. They could already hear the sound of engines and sirens as their pursuers drew close. "Grab what you can, and let's get out into the haystack," she said, kissing him.

Clyde took a BAR and satchel with extra clips. She took the shotgun and stuffed the safe contents back into the burlap sack. Then they slipped out the side door and, staying low, burrowed into the back of the haystack at the front of the barn.

Seconds later, six cars came streaming down the road and jammed up one after the other as the occupants—cops and the barons' men—spilled out and aimed their guns at the barn.

"We know you're in there," the sheriff called. "This doesn't have to end in a shoot-out and with you dead. You stole something that don't belong to you, and that's illegal. Come on out and face the consequences."

There was no movement, and the cops and armed thugs began cycling rounds into their guns.

Behind them, Clyde peeked his head up out of the straw and fired his .45 into the air.

"They're shooting," someone shouted, and everyone with a gun aimed it at the barn and opened fire.

They shot until they had to reload, riddling the old wood and sending long strips of kindling flying. After they reloaded, some shot more until they ran out again. In the ringing silence, attention riveted on the barn for any hint of life, the armed crowd moved closer.

Bonnie and Clyde slipped out of the haystack and crept into the last car in the line, a fancy one from the city muscle. The sheriff turned around just as they got moving.

"Shit, they're getting away," the sheriff yelled, swatting his hat against his leg in disgust.

"Correction," Clyde said. "We done got away." He pulled the pin from a grenade, courtesy of Sal's bag of tricks, and tossed it under the nearest car.

He slammed the newly liberated car in reverse and rattled down the dirt road as the cops and thugs scattered. The grenade exploded, ruining the car and crippling the next two as well, leaving their pursuers pinned between three burning cars and a bullet-ridden barn.

"That worked better than expected," Bonnie said.

"I never doubted your plan for a second," Clyde said.

CHAPTER 32

Drain the swamp

She studied the minutes of the hearing closely and sighed.
How men in power do drone on, she thought.

The appropriations hearing two days prior was infi-
nitely boring, tedious, and yet monumental in scope,
though few would know it.

Even though it was the weekend, she was dressed
professionally, wearing a black suit with a crisp white
blouse and high-heeled black pumps—her only
indulgence—unfit for walking. She looked across her
office at the closed door, her name stenciled in gold
letters on the other side of the dusty glass, and slipped her
shoes off to let her feet relax.

The hearing drew quite a crowd—the press corps
lining the first row of chairs, pens flying across the pages
of notebooks, camera flashes popping, trying to find a
story in all the posturing and carefully concealed begging.

The six men up front on that day—in high-backed
leather swivel chairs—were all white, all sixty or older,
and all US senators. Three puffed on cigars, inflaming
already florid cheeks. Staffers whispered in their ears
periodically, pouring ice water, coffee, and, in at least one
case, whiskey.

The agenda for the appropriations committee hearing
was lengthy. A dozen or so directors and officials lined up

to provide testimony, all brimming with confidence that their eloquence and bluster, their dire predictions and hopeful futures—or barring that, their influential home district contacts—would persuade these senators to open the federal government's purse strings.

A thin man with round, wire-framed glasses spoke about the budgetary needs of a new program to dismantle Prohibition. The senators alternated between grilling him and looking bored.

Flipping through the notes two days later was even more boring. She held her finger under a quote:

"By ensuring the government oversees liquor sales, we earn revenue on behalf of the American people, and we diminish the power of the criminal elements, the bootleggers, if you will, that rose up during Prohibition."

"Isn't that an excessive amount of regulation on the gentlemen now making liquors? We want to take that market away from the criminal elements, but not harm the legitimate businesses." *Senator from North Carolina*

"We don't think it is excessive."

"How exactly will this money be put to use for America?" *Senator from Arizona*

"The money will support the program until it becomes self-sustaining, and after that all revenues will be returned to the general fund."

That last piece was what interested her. She needed to tap into that funding to keep her own infant organization afloat.

The hearing ended before anything could be accomplished. There was an agenda for the following week, and she scanned the names of people scheduled to testify and the topics they would cover: funding the second part of the New Deal, the programs that would expand electrification into rural and agricultural areas, and one that would establish a minimum wage and maximum work week. She should be at those for sure.

The last topic was a bit of a dark horse: J. Edgar Hoover testifying about funding a scientific approach to fighting crime. Who was he? she wondered. And was he also trying to get his hands on off-the-books funding? Worth keeping an eye on.

She stretched her legs out on the table, flexing her calves.

Washington really felt like a swamp, sometimes. Hot and exotic, filled with decaying ideals and lurking dangers. But still a source of occasional beauty, like finding an orchid among the swamp grass.

The phone rang, startling her from her reverie. It was Reginald, from the White House.

"Do you have a date or event?" he asked.

"Hello to you too," she said.

"I don't have much time," he said. "We haven't heard a peep from you."

"I've got it under control, Reg," she said, knowing he hated that. "Relax and let me do my job."

"I don't take orders from a woman," Reginald said.

"This woman is the only thing standing between the president and the end of the glorious American experiment in democratic self-rule."

"If you shared some details, we could help."

"How did that work out last time?" she asked. "Money buys loyalty and the information that comes with it—especially in this town. He's got some good men close to him, and I've got my best two agents on the case."

"I think you're confusing 'agents' with 'farmers,'" he said icily.

"And I think you are confusing me with someone who gives a damn about your fragile little ego," she said. "Your lack of caution almost got the president killed. You know it, I know it, and he knows it. I will be in touch when I have something more specific." She dropped the phone in the cradle and enjoyed the thought of him turning red and apoplectic.

She returned to the transcripts, studying the decisions and looking for areas to exploit.

"Ah, the irony," she said to herself. "I need money to fight the power of money."

There was a rap at the door, and she jumped, instinctively slipping her shoes back on and then berating herself. She slid the desk drawer open and laid her hand on the pistol there. "Come in."

The door swung open. Carl held a crumpled piece of paper in his hand. "They just called from Pottsville. They're in trouble."

"Where the hell is Pottsville?"

CHAPTER 33

Home on the Grange

Hand-lettering arching above the doorway said, "City of Pottsville—Grange Hall."

Newly painted, the still-pristine white slats were lit golden in the thin dawn air. The building reminded Bonnie of the churches, the only buildings with money enough to afford paint, dotting the Texas plains of her childhood.

The memory of those days made her think of how often back then she had skipped church to lounge in bed and read Hollywood magazines. She cast her thoughts back to an adolescent obsession with becoming a film star. Her mother paid for glamour photos, and together they sent the pictures off to a dozen Hollywood producers. Only one bothered to respond: two cold sentences thanking her for her interest but declining. Bonnie had tearfully accused her mother of intentionally sending ugly photos, saying it was her fault they didn't want her in Hollywood—that she had sabotaged Bonnie's future.

Now, in the softening light of an eastern Pennsylvania morning, Bonnie felt embarrassed by her behavior, and wished she could tell her mother she was sorry.

"What's on your mind today?" Clyde asked, waking up and yawning, looking at her solemn profile as she gazed out the car's back seat window.

"Just thinking about the mistakes I've made," she said.

"I hope I'm not one of them," he said, sitting up.

"You're my biggest mistake," she said, "and also the best decision I ever made."

"Come on, let's take a look around," he said.

When they had arrived the night before, running without headlights, the hall was deserted, and they had parked behind the building next to the cornfield. They slept in the back seat with guns close at hand.

Now Clyde tried the side door. It was unlocked. "Goddamn it," he said. "We should have tried the door last night."

They walked into a large, empty room. At the far end was a stage. Benches faced the stage, and behind them, folding chairs were stacked against the back wall.

"Hello, anybody home?" Clyde yelled.

A man in overalls walked in behind them through the door they'd just used, surprising them both. Thin and wiry, he looked used to hard work and toughened up from years of it.

"Can I help you folks?" he asked suspiciously, eyeing their rumpled clothes and the bloody bandage on Clyde's hand where his cut-off fingertip had bled through.

"Sorry to barge in, but we got tired on our drive and thought this looked like a safe place to park overnight. And the missus here was hoping to, uh, powder her nose," Clyde said.

Bonnie smiled at the man warmly, and offered her hand. He shook it timidly but his suspicion faded away in the gaze of her easy expression, and he pointed. "There's one right behind the stage."

"That's mighty neighborly of you," Clyde said.

When Bonnie returned, her clothes straightened and

hair smoothed down, she unfolded a chair and sat down. "I feel like a new woman," she said. "This building is beautiful. Looks brand new."

"We're proud of our Grange hall," the man said. "And of the Grange in general. After all the bullshit that's—oh, sorry for cursing, ma'am—we feel damn, oh goddamn it." He was flustered now.

"I'm used to salty language," she said. "My father was a farmer."

"I never knew that," Clyde said, knowing full well her father was a bricklayer who died when she was a little girl.

"What does a Grange do, exactly?" Bonnie asked, ignoring Clyde and fluttering her eyes a little. It made sense to get more information about Sal's network.

"It's a place for us farmers and country folk to congregate, to learn new ways of farming, teach kids the value of farming—that kind of thing," he said. "And we work together to get laws passed favorable to rural life."

"Like what?" Clyde asked.

"Like free postal delivery to rural homes," he said.

"You did that?"

"We did," he said. "Used to have to pick up our mail in town. For some folks, that was a long way to go. Or they had to pay by the mile to get it delivered. That can cost a pretty penny."

"Bet there were some businesses none too happy about that law," Bonnie said.

"We want to make sure farmers and rural communities get a fair shake. We're working with the government now to bring affordable electricity to the countryside with the same kind of model. Say, I don't think I caught your names."

"Prentiss. Clarence and Brenda. We're Sal's friends," Clyde said, throwing that last bit out there, curious to see if it meant something.

"Why didn't you say so?" The man held out his hand, and Clyde took it. "I'm Ernie Shearer." He pumped Clyde's hand up and down. "We've heard about you—what you're doing."

Clyde and Bonnie looked at each other, surprised at the notoriety, and cautious.

"Sal should be here soon. We called late yesterday," Bonnie offered.

"Come on, we got a room in the back where you can rest and wash up," Ernie said.

He showed them to a modest guest room—a bunk bed and a small desk with a bible on it and a sink in the corner—and then said he'd round them up something to eat. Clyde stretched out on the lower bunk.

Bonnie pulled out the contracts and envelopes on Farquist and Dunthorpe from her bag and spread them out on the desk, tossing the bible onto the top bunk. She studied the receipts again. Close to a hundred dollars had been transferred to the dressmaker from Stubbs. Who was he buying such fancy clothes for, and was it really clothes or a cover for something else?

Bonnie pushed those papers aside and pulled out the photos of Dunthorpe, looking at the shadowy face of her lover, or what little of it she could see, given it was other parts of his physique that were visible. As much as she hated that woman, she couldn't help admiring her figure again. She looked like a real movie star. Bonnie felt a flush come over her cheeks.

She got up and locked the door. She wriggled into the bottom bunk with Clyde, nuzzling her lips into his neck and dragging her hand up along the inside of his thigh. She undid his belt buckle and slid her hand down his pants. Clyde kept his eyes closed but smiled as she slowly worked him up.

"Were you looking at them naughty pictures?" he said.

"What if I was?" she asked.

"I reckon we need to keep those around then," he said, shivering with pleasure as he entered her. "Or take some of our own."

"The last time we took pictures for a lark, the whole country thought I was a gun moll."

"There'd be no guns in the pictures I'm thinking about," he said with a whisper, finding a rhythm that caused the bed to shake into the wall.

"Hurry before Ernie gets back," she said, eyes closed.

"That shouldn't be a problem," he said with a groan, holding her shoulders tightly as he pushed into her.

Later, Bonnie and Clyde sat in the kitchen, sipping coffee, chatting with Ernie, and waiting for Sal. Ernie spread apple butter across four slices of bread and set down the plate in front of them.

"Guess the next part of the New Deal is pretty important to you all?" Clyde asked.

Before he had time to answer, the sound of car wheels on the gravel road outside the hall interrupted them, and Ernie looked out the kitchen window.

"It's Sal," he said. "I'll come back in a couple hours to see what you need. If by chance you've already moved on, I want to thank you now for your service to the people of our great country. You are heroes."

Before either Bonnie or Clyde could answer, Ernie left the kitchen. It had never occurred to either Bonnie or Clyde what they were doing was grand or high-minded, much less heroic. Like always, they were just trying to keep one step ahead of whatever was being thrown at them. When they were on the run, it had been the law. Now, well, it was one thing after the other, but it was still people trying to do them harm, and when that happened, their instincts kicked in.

"Heroes?" Bonnie asked. "That's a laugh."

"Not a term I ever expected to hear associated with either of us," Clyde said.

"Ernie must be a little tetched," Bonnie said.

"Soft in the head," Clyde said.

They peeked out the window. Two people got out of the car—Sal and Carl. Ernie greeted them, gestured at the hall and then got in his truck and drove off.

When Sal walked in, they were sitting at the table, eating and drinking coffee.

"Hey Sal, good to see you again, you know, without all the bleeding and missing fingers," Bonnie said.

"The police are looking everywhere for you," she said, irritated. "A hand grenade? Really? In Shitsville, Pennsylvania? Why not just take out an ad in the paper? You two have made a mess of things."

"No, no, we're fine," Bonnie said. "Thanks for asking. Want some coffee? Maybe a slice of bread with apple butter? It's delicious."

"I want you to tell me why you dragged me all the way up here," she said.

"We've got a lead," Bonnie said. "But we need to get out of here without any more attention."

"You could ride out of here on elephants and draw less attention," she said. "Tell me about the lead."

Bonnie spread out the receipts and the ledger and described the unusual expense of the gowns.

"We think it's worth checking out," she said.

Sal paused, and for an instant Bonnie worried her suspicion about the dress shop was wrong. Sal pulled a folded paper from her bag.

"This is the White House schedule. There are several

formal events coming up where the president will be highly vulnerable to an attack," she said. "If Stubbs is paying for someone to look the part to get into one of those events, the dresses are a reasonable thread on which to pull. Good work."

Bonnie was surprised, and then irritated, at how much this praise pleased her.

"Thanks, boss lady," Clyde said.

"Just 'boss,'" Sal said.

"We need to get to DC and figure out whose arm that well-turned-out gal is hanging on to," Clyde said.

"Lucky for you, I got you seats in a truck heading to DC from Pottsville today." She could barely contain her amusement. "It's a hog truck."

CHAPTER 34

Rats and weasels

"I'm on to something big here," Royce said. He was on a pay phone in front of the Hollywood Hills retirement community. "I just need a little more time."

His editor was unconvinced. "I need you doing your job."

"But Larry, I'm telling you, this is huge."

"You keep saying that, but I still don't know what it is."

"Please trust me on this. It's going to be huge, but I have to keep a lid on it."

"Royce, let me shoot straight with you," Larry said. "I need you in your seat churning out content for the little old ladies who buy our paper. This isn't the *Times* or the *Post*, and you're not Woodward or Bernstein. You're a decent writer, but you're thinking too big, always looking for a Pulitzer."

"I don't care about that," Royce said. "This is something in our own backyard, and it goes way up the chain."

"Look," Larry said. "Whatever you're doing, it's on you. This is vacation time, as far as I'm concerned. You run out of vacation, it's unpaid. And you better hope we don't fill your seat while you're out running around."

"Fine," Royce said. "I'll be back tomorrow."

"And don't be expensing any more trips on the company card," Larry said. "You tell me what the story is then we can have a different conversation."

Royce slammed the phone into the cradle and walked into the nursing home.

The woman at the desk looked at him with a pleasantly neutral expression. "May I help you?"

"I'm here to see Abe Schenkel," Royce said.

"Is he expecting you?"

"Hell yes, I'm expecting him," an old man said. He had rolled his wheelchair close to the front door. "I don't get a visitor in maybe five years, and you think I'd let this slip by? Expecting him? I've been waiting here since he called yesterday."

He was stooped and frail, but filled with energy. He reached out with both hands. "You must be Royce. I'm Abe. Come on back to what they call my room." He put his hand next to his mouth to feign a conspiratorial whisper. "It's really a closet with a bed. And a crapper."

Back in the room, which really was little more than a closet, he motioned for Royce to sit on the hard plastic chair and moved himself closer to the window. "I'm like a goddamned potted plant here," he said.

"Mr. Schenkel—"

"Abe, call me Abe."

"Abe, then. I'm here to talk about Randy Masterson."

His face darkened. "That rat, that weasel. Better call me Mr. Schenkel."

"I told you yesterday he was the person I wanted to learn more about."

Abe touched his forehead. "My memory, it's not so good. Did I tell you I was once a Hollywood big shot?"

"Yes, that's why I'm here," Royce said. "You worked with Randy Masterson."

"That rat, that weasel," Abe said. "Yeah, I worked with him—until he ran out on me."

"Will you tell me about that?" Royce asked.

"I don't know why the hell not? One day we're making the best monsters and corpses in the business. The phone was ringing off the hook, and the money was pouring in. The next day he was gone."

"Do you know where he went?"

"Who?"

"Randy Masterson."

"That rat, that weasel. We used to work together in Hollywood, you know. Real big shots."

"Right, but where did he go when he left?" Royce asked.

Abe waved his hand, brushing away the bad memory like it was a buzzing insect. "Who knows? I had to start from scratch. I did all right."

A nurse walked in with a tray of food. "We've got some lunch for you, Abe," she said. "Should we bring a plate for your friend?"

Royce looked at the tray—shreds of iceberg lettuce drowning in Italian dressing, a slice of meatloaf with congealed gravy, and an ice cream scoop of instant mashed potatoes.

Abe shook his head. "You call this lunch? I used to get better meals at the craft tables, and that was after the stars had their fill. Sweetheart, did I ever tell you I used to be a big shot in Hollywood?"

"Only every day," she said, patting his arm.

"The moxie on this one," Abe said, as she walked out smiling. "And nice gams too!" He wheeled over to the little table and began poking at the food, cutting the meatloaf into small bits and carefully matching them up with equal-size portions of potatoes.

Royce watched him for a while, thinking he would take a bite, but he was more intent on arranging the food.

"So, Abe, about Randy…"

"Randy Masterson?" he asked, annoyed. "That rat, that weasel. He ran out and took all our good stuff with him. The tools, the molds, the plastics, the wax. Never heard from him again." He looked out the window at a small, potted palm tree.

"Do you know where he went?" Royce asked.

"He sent me some candy. He left me marooned in Hollywood, and he sent me some goddamn candy."

"I don't understand," Royce said.

"Some honest-to-God southern divinity. It looked good. I don't know. I didn't eat it. His candy can rot in hell. I saved the box all these years so I could hand it to him as I passed by that rat, that weasel."

He rolled to the dresser and rummaged through some old photos, pens, and decks of cards, and pulled out a weathered box. The label said, "Granny's Southern Divinity. Handmade with love in Dallas, Texas." Tied to the outside of the box with a faded ribbon was an envelope. Abe opened it with his shaking hands and pulled out a folded piece of paper.

On the paper was a single word: Sorry.

"What do you think he was sorry for?" Royce asked.

"I don't know. He must have got into some kind of trouble." He leaned forward and lowered his voice. "Maybe with the mob. You know, the wise guys. Hollywood was thick with them back in the day. All I know is he showed up after a while and started talking to this agent about a book he wanted to write. I know this because I was shtupping his secretary, and she told me he had some big cover-up he wanted to make some money off of, and the next thing you know, his pretty young wife was dead, and he started writing crazy books nobody bought about Martian farmers taking over the world."

"You think his wife was killed?"

"Whose wife?" Abe asked.

"Randy Masterson. The rat, the weasel," he added, cutting Abe off.

"I don't know anything about that," Abe said. "Hollywood was a crazy town back then. Not like today."

He looked at the box of ancient candy, then up at Royce. "You want a piece of this?" he asked, opening it.

The candy inside had turned to dust, with the shriveled remains of pecans speckling the drifts. There was a newspaper clipping at the bottom and Royce pulled it out. It was an article with a black-and-white photo of Bonnie Parker's funeral. To the right of the picture, almost off-screen, a tall, thin man with wire-rimmed spectacles in priest's vestments was standing between the body and the press of onlookers.

"I'll be damned," Abe said. "It's Randy Masterson, that rat, that weasel. Dressed like a priest. Did I ever tell you we were big shots together in Hollywood?"

CHAPTER 35

Follow that pink dress

True to her word, Sal had a new car, a fancy change of clothes, and a fresh bag of tricks—with more cash and guns—waiting for them near the hog stockyard on the outskirts of DC. It was small comfort, given the stink they endured, penned up in a hidden compartment next to a truckload of squealing, shitting swine.

"I need a hundred baths," Bonnie said.

"My nose is ruined from trying to hold my breath for so long," Clyde said, fishing around under the seat looking for the guns. "I'll never forgive her for this."

"I'll never eat bacon again," Bonnie said.

They pulled up to the Mayflower Hotel, and the bellhop rushed to open the passenger car door. Bonnie, trying gamely to act couth despite an afternoon spent in a hog truck, held out her gloved hand for assistance and slid out of the car. She showed just a hint of thigh as her skirt rode up. Coming around the other side, Clyde pressed the car keys and a dollar bill into the young man's hand.

"There's more cabbage coming your way if you take good care of things now, you hear?" he said.

The bellhop nodded, and asked if they had luggage.

"No, dear boy," Bonnie said. "We're traveling light. Too light. I hear your dress shop is quite fine."

Her words spun out in some fake accent that was new and disorienting to Clyde's ear.

"The finest in the district," the boy said.

Clyde looked sideways at her as they walked toward the grand entrance on Connecticut Avenue.

"How'd you manage to shed that Texas drawl?" he said.

"I've been practicing," she said.

"When? We're together all the time."

"In my head, I guess," she said. "Fancy fake accents—that's what real spies do."

"We're spies now?" he asked. "Where are you supposed to be from?"

"I don't know—France or England or something."

"Better keep practicing," he said.

She stuck her tongue out at him, then stopped and caught his arm. "Oh look, Clyde. There's the tip of the Washington Monument." Bonnie pointed toward the river at the stone obelisk.

A second bellhop opened the heavy hotel doors. Clyde handed him a dollar, and the boy smiled broadly at his good fortune.

"You're getting used to being a big spender," Bonnie said, taking in the marble floors and columns, the dangling crystal chandeliers, the sprays of flowers, ornate rugs, and the hum of guests and workers walking through the grand lobby.

Bonnie noticed the concierge eyeing them curiously, and elbowed Clyde, nodding in the direction of the desk. He strode over to the counter, preemptively answering the question hovering on the concierge's face with his characteristic swagger, but with a twist this time.

"Good sir, I am parched and desire a whiskey as well as a cigar. My companion needs to visit your fine dress shop," he said. Bonnie smiled into her shoulder at the fake accent.

Clyde was too short to look down on the uniformed man standing behind the wooden counter, so he pushed back his fedora, and pinched his face into an inquisitive, pursed look. Bonnie took the cue, and stared up at the ceiling in a disinterested way, hoping she looked like a bored aristocrat by mimicking Angela Dunthorpe. The concierge paused for just an instant, and then snapped his fingers for a bellhop.

"Please show our guests to the gentleman's bar and the lady to the dress shop," he said.

Clyde pulled out a dollar bill and slid it across the mahogany counter. "I do appreciate the service, my good man," he said.

Clyde slipped his arm around Bonnie's waist as they walked down the grand hallway, reluctantly parting ways at the expanse of floor under the rotunda. The bellhop pointed out the bar to Clyde and then escorted Bonnie to the dress shop.

Inside the bar, a layer of blue smoke hung across the room like an ocean fog. Clyde instinctively counted off the people, assessing them for the level of threat they might pose. There were five men. Four huddled together over a table, smoking cigars and poring over some report, and one sat alone reading a newspaper business section. The only threat these doughy men posed was to the country's financial well-being, he thought, if even that.

Clyde sidled up to the bar and leaned against it. "Whiskey, neat, and make it a double," he said.

The bartender snapped a white linen napkin over his forearm as he pulled a tumbler from the shelf then reached for a bottle. Clyde mindlessly ate a few peanuts and then asked for a bowl of potato chips. The bartender set the glass down. It was a generous pour. Clyde was beginning to see the benefits of wealth.

"Must feel great to be back in business," Clyde said.

"Nobody was ever really out of business," the bartender said.

He was about the same age as Clyde's father, and thin, with gaunt cheekbones. He wore crisp, dark maroon slacks and a matching vest. Looked like a bellboy, Clyde thought, except without the monkey hat. "I worked at the education department through the Prohibition years," he said.

"The education department?"

"The bar up on Capitol Hill for the politicians," he said. "Inside the capitol and run by no less than the Speaker of the House."

"No kidding?" Clyde said. "Guess them laws about hooch was meant just for us little people."

Clyde tapped the glass, and the bartender poured another.

"You here on business?" the bartender asked.

"Of a sort, yeah," Clyde said. "My little lady is at that dress shop of yours."

Down the hall, Bonnie waited in the dress shop parlor for the shop girl. She looked at the showroom floor. A mother and daughter sat in plump chairs drinking tea and watching a parade of gowns for an impending cotillion.

A blonde model entered the room wearing a peach-colored, satin gown with matching gloves that reached past her elbows, her shoulders covered by a stiff tulle shawl. She circled the room, and then walked back into the dressing area.

The dress shop manager clapped, and another model circled the showroom, wearing a deep red velvet gown with a plunging neckline.

"A popular look this year," said the manager.

"Absolutely not," said the mother. "She looks like a harlot."

"I couldn't agree more," the manager said. She shooed the model out.

Bonnie watched the spectacle until a shop girl approached. "I'm sorry to keep you waiting, ma'am. How may I help you?"

Bonnie, who had been rehearsing the conversation in her head, snapped at her. "You can tell me why the dress my sister ordered never showed up today."

The shop girl, caught off guard by her vehemence, stammered and began to apologize. "I'm so sorry. What's your sister's name? Let me look at the delivery list."

Bonnie followed her to a small armoire desk on the side of the showroom. The manager looked over, but the hovering mother quickly diverted her attention.

"Don't show us any more dresses like that. They need to look, well…"

"Virginal?" said the manager.

The mother laughed. "We are trying to catch the eye of a certain kind of successful man." The daughter blushed.

"Your sister's name?" the shop girl asked.

"It was ordered under her employer's name, Mr. Stubbs."

"Yes, here it is. Stubbs. The last fitting was two days ago. The dress was delivered today."

"You must have the wrong address," Bonnie said. "She is just frantic."

"The delivery was made to the Willard Hotel, as requested," she said, looking at the notes in the ledger. "The event is tonight, so Miss Ballantine, your sister, was very specific about receiving the delivery today. We are on standby in case any last minute tailoring is required."

Bonnie let herself look chagrined. "That's the right address, so maybe the mix-up was at the hotel itself. I'm terribly sorry to have snapped at you."

The girl, used to being snapped at but unused to apologies, smiled. "It's no bother. I'll call the hotel immediately."

"That won't be necessary," Bonnie said. "I'm staying there myself, so I will inquire as soon as I get back. And just so I'm certain, it was the blue dress, right?"

The shop girl consulted her notes. "No ma'am, it was the pink dress."

"Yes, of course, pink. And full length?"

Bonnie noticed that the manager was looking more curiously at their interaction, and trying to free herself from the talkative mother. Time to close this one down, she thought. She looked at the shop girl.

"Yes, full length. Miss Ballantine was so excited about the party."

"Thanks so much," Bonnie said in a singsong voice. "You've been so very helpful," she said, loud enough for the boss to hear. Bonnie walked out of the dress shop and ducked into the bar. The bartender looked up.

"Ma'am, this is a men-only establishment," he said.

"Then you better pour me a glass of gin quick then, before anyone notices me," she said, putting her arm on Clyde's shoulder.

Clyde pushed over another dollar bill across the bar. "Humor her," he said.

The bartender poured a double for Bonnie.

Back in the dress shop, the shop girl was beside herself, thinking the mix-up might cost her this new job. She called the Willard Hotel and asked to be connected to Miss Ballantine's room.

CHAPTER 36

Three dead mice

Bonnie smiled at the hotel desk clerk. "I work at the Mayflower dress shop. A client was in recently and had her dress delivered here, but she left her pocketbook behind." She proffered a new handbag purchased moments earlier, with a few dollar bills sticking out. "Would you mind terribly making sure she gets it?"

"Of course. What is her name?" the clerk asked.

"Miss Ballantine," Bonnie said. "She had one of our loveliest dresses delivered here earlier—a pink, full-length gown."

"I believe she has gone out, but I'll make sure she gets it upon her return."

"You're a peach," Bonnie said brightly, turning. Clyde was standing behind her, and she touched her eyes and tilted her head, then walked past and into the lobby.

"I'd like to rent a room," Clyde said to the man as he watched the other reception clerk tuck the clutch into the mail slot for room 323. "Third floor if you have anything available. The wife has a thing about numbers." The man looked at him curiously. "Women," Clyde said. "What are you gonna do?"

Later, after a drink in the bar to steady their nerves, they stood in front of 323. Clyde pulled his gun and made ready to kick the door in, but Bonnie shook her head and pushed him to the side of the door.

"We don't want her to know we've busted in," she whispered. She knocked. "Housekeeping. I have those extra pillows you called for." There was no sound, and she rapped again. "Housekeeping. May I come in?"

They stood there for a minute without a response from inside the room. A maid turned the far corner, and Clyde slipped his gun out of sight.

"I need you to yell at me," Bonnie whispered. "Make like I locked the key inside."

"Now I have to walk all the way back to the front desk," Clyde yelled. "And all because you can't keep a single thought in that pretty little head of yours."

"I'm real sorry, honey," she said, lip quivering as the maid drew closer. "I didn't mean to."

"Didn't mean to, didn't mean to," he roared. "You never mean to do half the stupid stuff you do. But I told you to put the key in your purse before we left."

"May I help you folks?" the girl asked, looking at Bonnie with concern.

"Only if you can teach Dumbo here how to use her brain," Clyde said, feigning exasperation.

"I left our key inside," Bonnie said, pulling her body in on itself, trying to be small, and casting her eyes pitifully to the floor.

"Oh honey, let me get that door for you," the maid said. "It's no trouble." She shook the key ring at her waist and opened the door. Clyde brushed past her.

"Right by the bed where we left it," he said, triumphantly, holding up their key with the room number hidden behind his thumb.

"You ought not to let him yell at you like that," the girl whispered.

"Thank you so much for helping me out," Bonnie

said, feeling a little ashamed at taking advantage of her kindness. Bonnie pushed the door closed, and they were alone in the luxury suite, battling that sick, empty-stomach feeling of being in someone else's world.

Clyde stood in the closet looking at the clothes. Dresses and petticoats and ladies' shoes. Bonnie saw a bottle of perfume on the dresser and picked it up. "This is Joy, by that French fellow, Jean something. I've been dying to try it."

She dabbed a little on her wrists and rubbed them together. "Smell."

He leaned in close and breathed deep. It smelled like flowers, jasmine, and roses, but a little sickly sweet—like a funeral with way too many lilies—and he wrinkled up his nose. "Doesn't smell as good as you do after a bath," he said. "But at least it helps hide the hog stink."

"You do not have refined tastes, Clyde Barrow," she said, returning her attention to the closet. "Not a single jacket or pair of pants in here. Maybe she doesn't know her moneybags man is a killer."

He left her flipping enviously through the clothing, and looked in the main part of the foyer. A map of DC was spread out on the table, creased to highlight the White House and pencil marks traced several of the avenues toward Union Station.

"Oh, she knows. Looks like they've got escape routes planned." He picked up another sheet of paper—this one the president's itinerary. "There's some sort of shindig at the White House tonight."

"That has to be it," Bonnie said. "Come and take a look at this." She had pulled a suitcase out from under the bed. It contained some loose bullets scattered at the bottom, a long, thin stiletto knife in a forearm sheath, and leftover bands from stacks of money.

"Looks to me like we're dealing with some tough customers," he said.

"Why leave all this behind?" Bonnie asked. "It'd make it clear they were up to no good."

"Does seem odd," Clyde said. He was admiring the knife, drawing a tiny bead of blood from the needle-sharp tip when he touched it against his thumb.

"The lights are still on in the bathroom," Bonnie said. She walked toward the door.

Clyde followed, knife in hand, and looked up as she started to push the door open. In the reflection of the vanity mirror, he saw a small, brown bottle perched on the top of the door, dislodged by the motion. He snaked his hand out and caught it in midflight.

"Smart. A bottle of perfume smashed on the floor would be a dead giveaway that someone has been snooping around." He unscrewed the cap and took a sniff, then wrinkled up his nose.

He started to dab some on his finger to taste it, and Bonnie caught his arm. "Wait, don't touch it," she said, pointing inside the bathroom.

More bottles filled with liquids of various shades were scattered on the vanity next to a set of beakers, test tubes, and lipstick containers. Next to it all was a cage with three white mice, all dead.

"They're gonna poison the president," Clyde said.

Bonnie, heart thumping, opened a small case. It was thickly padded and had an empty slot about the size of the bottle Clyde was holding. A label inside the lid spelled out just how close they had just been to a fiery death: *Danger: Explosive. Nitroglycerin. Handle with extreme care.*

"If that bottle had hit the floor, it would've set off an explosion big enough to turn this whole room inside out," Bonnie whispered.

Clyde looked at the bottle in his hand. "Guess they ain't planning on coming back," he said.

"They intended to kill that sweet little maid who defended me against you, or one just like her. And probably half a dozen other people as well."

"Destroying all evidence in the process," he said. He carried the vial out into the front room and laid it on a cushion.

"There isn't anyone lower than a poisoner," Bonnie said.

"You'll get no argument from me on that," Clyde said. "You got a plan?"

"Yeah," she said. "We need to get into that party."

CHAPTER 37

Champagne before crashing

"Think Sal can get us into that soiree?" Clyde asked. He was standing by the window, looking down at the city bustling with early evening activity, and at the lush, green grounds surrounding the nearby White House.

"There's no time to contact her," Bonnie said. "We have to crash it." She was in the bathroom of their suite at the Willard Hotel. "Damn bathroom is bigger than the bedroom I grew up in," she said, splashing her face with cold water.

"You want us to crash the White House," he said. "That's your plan?"

"No," she said, patting her face dry on an obscenely plush towel that, she swore, would go home with her, even though she had no idea where home was anymore. "That's the desired outcome. I don't have a plan, yet, for how we do it."

She looked in the mirror. The days of running were taking their toll, and the afternoon in the hog truck didn't help. She pulled at the dark circles under her eyes, smoothed the oily hair plastered to her head, and was dismayed by the permanent furrow beginning to take shape between her eyebrows.

She sighed and turned away from her reflection, sat on the edge of the bathtub and ran some water. "One thing is certain—we can't go looking like hobos."

She carefully pulled off her stockings, tugging gently at the material that had lightly stuck to the last of the scabs on her leg, and slid into the tub. As the warm water washed away the grime and stress, she called out to him. "Clyde, what's this party for again?"

He pulled out the itinerary liberated from the assassin's room. "A celebration of the passage of the Securities Exchange Act," he said.

"What's that?" she asked.

He picked up the newspaper on the nightstand. "It's covered right here on the front of the paper." He skimmed the article. "Something about making sure stocks are real and registered with the government so everyone knows they are legit, so that nobody gets swindled no more, I guess."

"They don't have to do that now?" Bonnie asked, rinsing her hair.

"Guess not," Clyde said.

She hauled herself out of the tub, cutting the bath criminally short, and wrapped herself in one of the robes that, like the towel, would be hers now. She padded back into the main room.

"Get cleaned up," she told Clyde, "and dress up fancy, but not too fancy."

"I got limited clothing options," he said. He still wore the suit Sal had given him days ago when all this first started.

"Let's at least get it pressed," she said.

"Yes ma'am," he said, stripping as she picked up the telephone on the writing desk. "We got time for a quickie? This may be our last night together."

She looked him up and down, smiling and glad to see he was getting hard for her just thinking about it, but shook her head. "They'll be plenty of other times," she said, dialing room service. "Send up a bottle of champagne and two glasses. And we need a suit pressed."

While Clyde cleaned up, she lit a cigarette and picked up the paper. The headline read: Fourteen million out of work; drought forces thousands off farms. Beneath the headline there was a photo of a vortex of wind whipping up the soil in Oklahoma and another photo of a beat-up pickup truck packed full of family belongings. A tired woman stood in front of the truck, holding a baby in one arm, with two toddlers hanging on her skirt. Strands of hair blew across her soiled face.

Bonnie sighed. The woman looked so sad, so hopeless, like the woman in the truck headed to California who made her man stop to help just a few days ago near Dallas. She pulled deep on the cigarette and opened the paper, looking at other articles. She sat up straight and stubbed out the cigarette.

"How interesting," she said. "Seems like Eleanor Roosevelt held one of her ladies-only press conferences today."

"Ladies only?" Clyde asked, coming out of the bathroom in a robe.

"She's got this thing where she only invites female reporters to her meetings," Bonnie said.

"Lady reporters?" he asked. "Didn't know there was such a thing."

Bonnie picked up a pen lying on the desk. She grabbed a piece of hotel stationery from the drawer. She stood up, and her face took on a serious look.

"Now tell me, sir, what do you feel are the most important elements of this...um." She faltered, looked at the itinerary again, and scanned it quickly. "How will the Securities Exchange Act help the forgotten man?" She held the pen poised to write on the stationery.

"Bonnie, this ain't really the time for joking around," Clyde said. "We got a real problem on our hands and…" He grinned. "Baby, you done it again."

"You can be my photographer," she said. She reached for the phone and called the concierge again. "Yes, I'm a reporter with the *Dallas Morning News*, part of Mrs. Roosevelt's lady press corps. Our luggage was misplaced, and we have an event in about an hour. We need a good, solid camera, a steno pad and a box of pencils, sharpened. Can you do that? Very good. See you in an hour then."

She hung up and looked at him triumphantly.

"It's a good plan, but how do we know they'll let us in? Won't we need, you know, credentials?"

"That's where your charm and a little luck will come in," she said.

There was a light knock at the door. "Room service, sir," a voice called.

Clyde let in the waiter, who brought the champagne in a bucket of ice, and he popped the cork for them. "The rest of your items will be here within the hour."

"Thanks," Clyde said, slipping him a dollar.

When the waiter left, Clyde poured them each a glass of bubbly. "To that powerful brain of yours," he said.

She clinked his glass, took a sip, and raised hers. "To more than enough time for a quickie," she said, taking him by the hand and pulling him toward the bed.

"I'll drink to that anytime," he said.

CHAPTER 38

Bureaucratic glamour

Bonnie pulled lightly on the corners of Clyde's bow tie, straightening it.

"It's too tight," Clyde said, tugging at his collar.

"It's perfect," she said. "You look handsome all dressed up—like a movie star."

He grinned and caught her by the hips and pulled her close. "Handsome enough for a little hanky-panky?"

She wriggled out of his clutches with a laugh. "You're never satisfied."

"Not when it comes to you, I'm not," he said.

She slipped her arms around his neck. "And I'm thankful for that. But just for tonight, we are not a couple. You're my photographer, and I'm a lady reporter," she said. "We just got here from Texas."

"Yeah, well, we could be a couple who are sneaking around with each other at the office," he said. "Everybody knows that's how it goes. Gives our cover story more believability."

Bonnie rolled her eyes and dropped the camera around his neck. "Come on, let's go."

They waited in line at the White House gate with the crowd of partygoers. The women pulled their fur stoles and shawls tight in the cool evening breeze.

"Clyde, pinch me. I can't believe it. We're going into

the White House," Bonnie said. "The White House."

"We ain't in there yet, Bon," he said.

"You ready?" she said.

He nodded and held up the camera.

"You even know how to use that thing?" she whispered.

"Watch me." Clyde nudged the couple in front of them. "Excuse me, little lady. Coming through, sir," Clyde said, elbowing his way up to the front of the line. "Step aside, make way."

"What are you doing?" Bonnie said. "Clyde, stop." But it was too late.

A social secretary stood at the entry point, politely collecting the invitations as the guests filed through the iron gates. When she moved, fringes on the bottom hem of her lilac-colored, knee-length dress swayed back and forth.

"Invitation please?"

"Smile wide for the *Dallas Morning News*, darlin'," Clyde said.

The bulb flashed. The secretary smoothed her hair back automatically, but then caught herself.

"Ain't you a lovely thing," Clyde said, an affable grin spreading across his face.

Turning on the charm, Bonnie thought. She followed him to the front of the line. The guests murmured disapproval, but let her pass.

"I'm sure our lady readers in Dallas will enjoy admiring your lovely, fashionable dress," Bonnie said, reaching the front of the line. "As for that invitation, well, it went missing, along with our luggage on the train from Dallas."

"What's your name? I'll check it against the list."

"Brenda Prentiss. I'm a lady reporter from the *Dallas*

Morning News, and this here is my photographer, who does sometimes get ahead of himself." She wagged her finger playfully at Clyde. The secretary picked up a list from the desk and scanned it. "I don't see your name here, ma'am."

"Miss Eleanor herself invited me to the Ladies Press Conference today and because of the incompetence of that railroad we lost everything. I had to borrow this dress, can you imagine? Even worse, I missed Miss Eleanor's meeting," she said, loud enough so the impatient guests in the front of the line could hear. "Isn't that just the most awful thing?"

Bonnie turned to the people behind her, hoping for nods of approval. The tuxedos, top hats, furs and gowns blurred into a single image, and she frowned at their whisperings. Uncouth. Who let the Texans in? That dress looks awful. How dare they cut in front of us.

The secretary nodded to a uniformed Secret Service officer standing nearby, who walked toward them. Bonnie saw that any small advantage from Clyde's impromptu bluster was about to slip away. No turning back now, she thought.

"Now listen up, I've got a story to write about this party for my paper. They paid a lot of money to send me, and I will write it, and we're going to take some pretty pictures of fancy ladies to go with it," Bonnie said, her voice rising.

A flash popped again. Clyde had turned the camera on the waiting guests. The officer stopped next to Clyde and smiled patiently but resolutely.

Clyde looked up at him and winced. "You are a tall one, ain't you? This pretty good work here at the White House? You like being a doorman and keeping all the riffraff out?"

"No more photos," the man said. "Please vacate the premises or you'll spend the night in jail."

An older couple moved forward. The man brushed hard against Clyde, causing him to stumble. His companion, a gray-haired woman with a fortune in diamonds around her neck, dramatically averted her eyes to avoid looking at Bonnie.

"Now, just a minute," Clyde said. "Nobody pushes me." He balled his hand into a fist and Bonnie knew the situation was about to spin out of control.

She put her hands on her hips and faced the social secretary for one last try. "I don't want to be rude, but we've come a long way and intend to show the president in the finest light possible to the citizens of the great state of Texas," she said. "And you have no right—"

Clyde nudged her and tilted his head toward the line of guests.

A woman in a long, black coat made her way through the waiting crowd. People seemed to recognize her, politely letting her pass. "Brenda, and your able photographer," Sal said, reading the situation. "I was worried you weren't going to make it."

She offered her credentials to the social secretary. "They're with me."

"Yes ma'am," she said. "Please go on through. I'm sorry for the inconvenience."

Bonnie and Clyde silently followed Sal onto the White House grounds, through the open doors and into a grand foyer. As she led them down a marbled corridor and they gazed through the doors leading into the spacious East Room, Bonnie and Clyde felt like they had entered another world—candelabras and ceiling frescos; elegant men and women laughing and making small talk; waiters moving with ease through the room, balancing silver trays loaded with drinks and food. Classical music filled the air.

"Get a load of this place," Clyde said.

"What the hell were you thinking?" Sal asked, cutting into their star-struck reveries. "Crashing the White House? What would you have done if I hadn't shown up?"

"His charm and a little luck was all we needed. I guess you were our luck."

"Why are you here?" she asked.

"The assassin will be at the event tonight," Clyde said. "We just have to look for a lady wearing a—"

A butler interrupted and offered to take Sal's coat. She nodded and shrugged out of the wrap, revealing a floor-length, pink gown. She watched him carry her coat toward a coatroom and then turned back to Bonnie and Clyde, who were staring at her, their mouths hanging open.

"You were saying. A lady wearing what?" Sal asked.

"A pink, floor-length gown," Bonnie said.

CHAPTER 39

Pick your poison

"If you're here with the killer, things are about to get really complicated," Clyde said to Sal, slipping the stiletto he'd stolen from the hotel room out of the forearm sheath. He grabbed her by the wrist and laid the tip of knife lightly against her sternum. Bonnie wondered again who the bad guys actually were in this crazy situation.

"What the hell are you doing?" Sal hissed.

"The assassin is here with some kind of rat poison and a woman in a pink dress," he said. "You're in a pink dress. You can see how that would lead us to think you're here with the assassin."

"This is my one good formal dress," Sal said. "I've had it for years. If you get blood on it, so help me God, I will skin you both alive."

"It's true," Bonnie said. "This dress went out of style before I was in grade school. Not likely one made recently by that fancy dress shop."

"You try to get by on a civil servant salary," Sal said. "Put the knife away and tell me what you know."

Clyde slipped the blade away and pretended to line up the perfect photo while Bonnie held her pad and pretended to take notes, instead leaning in close to bring Sal up to speed.

"So we are looking for any man who's with a woman

in a floor-length, pink gown?" Sal asked.

"I see two—three, counting you," Clyde said, still suspicious.

"Are you sure it's poison?"

"Ask the three dead mice in the Willard, Room 323," Bonnie said. "Also, if you send someone to investigate, there's a bottle of nitroglycerine on a sofa cushion in the front room. Handle it with care."

"I'm going to mingle. Let me know what you find out," Sal said.

They watched her leave. "We still don't know what her real name is," Clyde said. "If we could get a look at that invite list, at least we could narrow it down to a couple hundred people."

"We may have to wait," Bonnie said. "The president is already here."

Roosevelt was seated near the far wall, surrounded by an entourage. His wife stood to his left, and to the right was a large man in an ill-fitting suit—he looked like a stone carving, with hands the size of shovel blades and a cauliflower nose that had been broken so many times it quit trying to stay straight.

"That's the president?" Clyde said. "He looks a lot smaller in person. Or maybe it's just the gorilla standing next to him."

A line of men and women waiting to greet the president was forming. Bonnie and Clyde watched as a woman in a pink, floor-length gown and her companion—a dark-haired man with an extravagant mustache oiled into twists—approached. After their introductions, they laughed and chatted with the First Lady and president until the woman excused herself to go to the bar. She ordered two glasses of champagne. From across the room, Bonnie and Clyde watched her tip a small bottle into the flutes.

"This is it," Clyde said.

They hightailed across the room and stood on either side of her as she picked up the glasses.

"The jig is up, sister," Bonnie whispered, pressing the barrel of her little .25 into the woman's back. "You move, you even squeal, I put a bullet into you. Down low, in your spine, so you never waltz again. Got it?"

The woman nodded, her eyes shocked and wide.

"Make a beeline for the ladies room and maybe you live," Bonnie said.

They guided her across the floor, and she looked back over her shoulder at the man. "But what about Donald?" she asked.

"Forget your partner," Bonnie said, jabbing her with the gun. "It's just us now."

They half pushed and half dragged her into the alcove in front of the bathrooms.

"What is this about?" She still held a glass of champagne in each hand.

"Don't play cutesy," Clyde said. "We know you're trying to kill the president."

"Kill the president? What are you talking about?" the woman asked, almost in tears. "Is this some kind of joke?"

"You're good, lady," Bonnie said. "Real smooth. But we saw you put the poison in the glass."

"Poison?" the woman responded, incredulously.

"Yeah, the poison. In the little bottle. You put it in the glasses."

"You mean the Campari for our champagne?"

"The what?" Bonnie asked.

"The Campari. It's a bitter. A kind of drink. My husband I both enjoy it from our time in Italy." She was relaxing a little and took a sip. "See?"

"You've got two glasses. How stupid do you think we are?" Clyde asked.

She took a sip from the other glass. "Pretty stupid, I guess. Are you his bodyguards or something? If so, you're not doing a very good job."

"Darling," the man with the mustache said, turning the corner. Sal was beside him. "Where are you taking our drinks, and who are these people?"

"They are from the Dallas paper," Sal said, catching him by the arm. "One of Eleanor's lady reporters, Brenda, and her photographer, Clarence. Let me introduce Donald and Cookie Smith. Donald worked for the consulate in Italy."

Bonnie slipped her gun out of sight. "Cookie was just telling us all about the Campari you enjoy in your champagne. We're sorry for keeping you so long, and hope it won't reflect poorly on our employer." She shot a pleading look at Cookie.

"Your employer has peculiar standards," she said, arching her eyebrow.

"Very good then," Donald said. "Some of our friends from the Italian embassy stopped in. They are dying to say hello to Cookie."

Cookie smiled thinly at Bonnie and Clyde. "It was a lovely chat. I hope the rest of your evening is more, shall we say, productive."

Head hanging low, Clyde watched them return to the main room. "It wasn't them," he said.

"Clearly," Sal said. "He's been in the foreign service for years."

"How could we have known that?" Bonnie asked. "It's not like we're trained spies or anything. We're just making this up as we go."

"Make it up better," Sal said. "If anything happens to the president, I'm out of a job, and the country is up shit creek." She straightened the hem of her dress. "Oh, and you're dead, and your entire family is in jail for at least two generations."

"Why don't you just tell him he's in danger and let the professionals take care of him?"

"He knows he's in danger," Sal said. "Maybe not exactly how much danger, but he can't spend his term looking over his shoulder and wondering what new enemies he's made trying to save us from the industrialists. Plus we don't know who we can trust."

"We're still wondering who 'we' is," Bonnie said.

"Just do your job."

She shooed them back around the corner and into the ballroom where they all three stopped dead in their tracks.

A tall woman was handing the president a tumbler filled with a whiskey. She was wearing a floor-length, pink gown.

CHAPTER 40

The power of pimento cheese sandwiches

"Wait, you thought Sal was the assassin, and then the Italian diplomat named Cookie?" Royce asked. "How could you be so wrong?"

"Royce, we were so far out at sea. Everywhere we turned there was danger, lies, and intrigue," she said.

"Hard to imagine what that must have been like," Royce said.

The micro-recorder came to a stop, and he popped it open, flipped the tape cassette and hit record again. The recorder whirred back into action, and he set it down between them on the bench.

They sat together in a small town park across from Lubbock City Hall. Bonnie had called Royce to tell him she was coming into town for some errands, and preferred to have their interview there, saying she was hankering for a change of scenery. It was lunchtime, and the little patch of green was filled with office staff taking a noontime break.

Bonnie opened the brown paper bag and pulled out two pimento cheese sandwiches in plastic baggies. "I made one for you. Would you like it?"

"Sure," he said, unwrapping the sandwich and taking a bite. "Damn, that's good."

"Hard to mess up pimento cheese," she said. She

twisted open a thermos and poured what looked like water into the thermos cap.

"Want a sip?"

He shrugged and took a sip, then sputtered. "What the hell is that?" he asked.

"Gin with a little tonic," Bonnie said. "What else?"

He wiped his mouth with his sleeve, leaving a trace of cheese along his jacket, and took another slug. She ate a few bites of her sandwich and then switched to gin.

"In those early days, we were reacting so fast to everything that was thrown at us, we didn't really have much time to think any of it through," she said. "That came later. The thinking-through part, I mean."

Bonnie's eyes drifted toward a young couple sitting on the bench across from them. The woman skillfully laughed at something unfunny the man said.

"She's trying too hard," Bonnie said, smiling ruefully. "That couple is just about the same age as when Clyde and I first met."

"I'm kind of on the edge of my seat here," he said. "I want to know what happened to the president. I mean, he didn't die, did he, replaced by an exact replica—like at your funeral? Or maybe aliens came down and now run the country?"

He felt immediately embarrassed by his sarcastic tone. Bonnie paid him no mind, watching the young couple as they stood and walked back toward City Hall, holding hands. Bonnie followed them with her eyes as they walked up the steps. The man opened the door, and the woman walked through.

"Would have been nice to have a different kind of life with Clyde, but I'm not really one for regrets," she said. "We did have some good years together at the end—peaceful years—although they came at quite a cost."

She took another sip of the gin. "Mind if I ask you a few questions?" she asked.

"Not at all," Royce said, grateful she was ignoring his alien remark.

"You making progress on figuring things out?"

"A little," he said. He pulled out the newspaper clipping Abe Schenkel gave him at the old folks home and handed it to Bonnie. "Look familiar?"

"That's a photo of my funeral," she said. "No offense, Royce, but there's lots of them around."

"Do you know the man standing near the casket?"

"There were so many people there, most of 'em gawkers," she said.

"I mean the preacher."

She looked more closely, and her eyes clouded as her memories shot back in time. "I remember seeing him. He kept folks from getting too close. Took my arm when I faltered."

"His name is Randy Masterson. I think he may be the one who doctored up the bodies to look like you," Royce said.

Bonnie looked harder at the photo and shook her head. "How could a preacher do that?" she asked.

"He wasn't a preacher," Royce said. "He was a Hollywood special-effects man. Dead now. I talked to his daughter a few days ago and his business partner yesterday. His partner was a bit gone with dementia, but it seems likely Masterson made fake bodies for you and Clyde then never worked in Hollywood again."

Bonnie looked up at him, startled. "My death was faked by Hollywood?"

"Maybe."

She laughed quietly. "Well, that's something else. Like I always say—be careful what you wish for."

Royce looked at her quizzically. "What do you mean?"

"There was a time before I met Clyde when my big dream was to be a Hollywood movie star," she said. "My momma always said I was pretty enough."

She handed the newspaper clipping back to Royce. "Does this mean you believe me?" she asked.

"I'm getting close, but I need more," he said. "I need something to verify all this. Something you can show me to set my mind at ease."

She looked at him curiously. "Well, come on, spit it out."

He smiled. Despite himself, he was growing fond of this curious old woman. Still, he had to ask. Go on, he thought, get it over with.

"Bonnie Parker was burned pretty bad in a car crash right before she—I mean you—died."

"That's right," she said. "Clyde was driving like a maniac, lost control and crashed. The car caught on fire and burned me badly before he could get me out. Like, really badly." She rested her hand on her thigh.

"Must have left some pretty nasty scars," he said.

"You want to see my leg?" she asked. "You must be desperate for action if you want to see an old lady's gams."

"I don't want to, but I kind of need to," he said. "Physical evidence is important in these situations." He took another bite of the sandwich and tried to block out just how crazy and awkward this had become.

"If I was going to go this far in telling such an elaborate untruth, wouldn't I have taken care of that?" she asked.

"I suppose so," he said. "Cosmetic surgery. Or maybe the scars were from something else, and you just built the story on top of them. Either way, without the scars the story falls apart. With the scars, we keep going."

"Fair enough," Bonnie said. She stood up with some difficulty and pulled up her black skirt. Underneath, she wore no stockings, just a white satin slip.

"Not here," he said, looking around. "We can do it later. Someplace private. Please. Stop."

"I'm an old woman with no use or time for decorum," she said.

A deputy walked by on the way to City Hall and slowed, looking suspiciously at the elderly woman hiking up her skirt. Bonnie waved him on. "Nothing to see here," she said. "Keep on moving."

She bared her thighs. Even against the loose and wrinkled skin, Royce could make out a river of raised scar tissue, like the ruddy mudflat bottom of a low-flow river.

"Good enough?" she asked.

"Yes, yes, good enough," he said. "Sit down, please."

She did, and poured herself more gin.

"I'm sorry," Royce said. "Maybe I crossed the line."

"I admire thoroughness," Bonnie said. "That's why I picked you." She balled up the empty plastic sandwich wrapper and put it into her purse, along with the brown paper bag.

"Now where was I in my recollecting?" she asked. "Oh, right—saving the president."

CHAPTER 41

On the rocks

Without a word, Bonnie raced across the room, Clyde close on her heels.

"Brenda Prentiss from the *Dallas Morning News*," she said, leaning in close to the startled group. "How about a picture, maybe without the booze, to celebrate this momentous evening?"

"That'd be just fine," the president said. He smiled and handed the tumbler back to the woman, who glared at Bonnie.

Clyde snapped a photo of the president and watched the woman walk away angrily. "Hold on darling, don't you want to be famous?" he asked, following the woman in the pink dress across the crowded room. Bonnie watched them go, knowing Clyde would corner and trap the assassin.

"She just stole your drink, Mr. President," Bonnie said. "Let me go get you another one."

"I won't try to stop you," the president said. "But make sure it's really neat this time? Why water down perfection?"

"Why indeed?" Bonnie said. She walked back to the bar and nodded at Sal as they passed. Sal breathed a sigh of relief and walked toward the far end of the room.

Bonnie caught the eye of the bartender, a tall woman

with dusky skin, dark eyes, and black hair pulled back into a tight braid.

"Could I get a whiskey for the president," Bonnie said. "Better make it a double." She sat down on one of the stools and put her pad and pencil on the bar. "And neat."

The woman turned her back to Bonnie and busied herself dropping ice cubes into a glass, struggling to use the tongs effectively with white gloves on, and then filled it with whiskey.

She turned and smiled and set the glass in front of Bonnie.

"Thanks," Bonnie said, but then noticed the ice. "Didn't I say it was neat?"

"Yes," the bartender said. "It is neat. A real neat event. I'm pleased to be here."

"No, I mean the drink," Bonnie said. "It's supposed to be neat. No ice."

A look of irritation flashed across the bartender's face. "Sorry, I misheard." She dumped the contents in the sink and tossed the glass into the trash, then turned her back once again and filled a new glass. When she turned around, the irritation had been replaced by a practiced smile. She set the fresh glass on the bar, the gloves causing her to lose her grip and slop a little over the edge. She quickly peeled off her gloves and threw them away.

"Maybe a coaster would be nice," Bonnie said. "You seem pretty new at this."

"And you seem pretty new at being a lady journalist," the bartender said, nodding toward the pad, which was filled with doodles.

"I guess we're both new to our jobs then," Bonnie said, picking up the glass.

"Wait, please don't say anything," the bartender said. "I really need this job."

Bonnie smiled. "Don't worry. It's our little secret."

As Bonnie crossed the floor she paused long enough to let a server pass, a young woman who kept one arm behind her back as she expertly balanced a tray with puff pastries stuffed with deviled ham. As she got closer to the president, she could see the bartender at the second bar at the far end of the room shake a martini with efficiency borne of experience. And he wasn't wearing gloves.

She bent down to hand the drink to the president and then paused, the drink just out of his reach.

He looked at her curiously. "Young lady, I'm the president of the United States, and I command you to give me my drink," he said with a twinkling smile.

"I'm sorry sir. It just struck me that she put a splash of bitters in here." She straightened up and shot a quick look at the bar. The bartender was gone. "I'll be right back," she said.

"I swear, it's easier getting Congress to pass laws they don't like than it is for me to get a drink in my hand. And now the bartender has abandoned her post. Will someone go get me a double whiskey, neat, before I declare war on this celebration," the president said. The men and women surrounding him laughed at his joke.

Bonnie walked back to the now deserted bar, dumped the drink into the sink and tossed the glass into the trash. There was a little brown vial, like the one they'd seen beside the dead mice, on top of the discarded gloves.

Poison, she thought, looking around quickly. The bartender was the killer.

With Clyde chasing the wrong pink dress and Sal nowhere to be seen, she was on her own. She slipped her gun out of her purse and pushed into the side room where the food was brought up from the downstairs kitchen, and waiters filed in and out to take the silver trays laden with delicacies to the guests. The room was bustling with activity, but no sign of the bartender.

"May I help you, ma'am?" one of the butlers asked.

"I'm looking for the bartender. She said she had a cocktail recipe for me. Tall gal, kind of dark looking."

"The new girl. She just passed through," he said. "Maybe she was going out for a smoke."

Bonnie kept the little pistol out of sight as she ran into the adjacent servants' hall. It was deserted, and she walked quietly down the length of it, testing the doors lining each side. One closet door was unlocked, and she pushed it open, gun at the ready. She held her hand to her mouth at the sight of a young woman, her hands bound and her throat slit. She was wearing black pants and shoes, but her shirt was missing.

"Oh you poor thing," Bonnie whispered. "You must be the real bartender."

She saw shadowy movement out of the corner of her eye and tried to duck, but something heavy struck her across the skull and darkness flooded out from the point of impact, narrowing her vision as she keeled face-first onto the cold breasts of the closet corpse.

Back in the East Room, Clyde hurried in, camera forgotten. He scanned the room and, not spotting Bonnie, headed directly for Sal, who was chatting with the Smiths and several others. By this time, the room was crowded with guests. He pushed through and caught Sal's arm.

"We've got a problem," he said.

"With your article?" she asked, arching her eyebrow.

"Yeah, the article." He led her to a quiet spot. "Where is Bonnie?"

"You mean Brenda," Sal said.

"I mean Bonnie," he snarled.

"What's wrong?" she asked, looking worriedly over at

the president.

"That gal in the long pink dress I followed ain't the assassin. In fact, she's dead. I watched her take one sip of that whiskey meant for the president and then keel over, foaming at the mouth and twitching."

"The only person who could have poisoned the whiskey was the bartender…" Sal said, her voice trailing off. "That means the assassin is still on the loose."

"Yeah. And since Bonnie and that bartender are both gone, something tells me Bon figured it out," Clyde said.

A warbling shriek rose from the hall behind them.

"They must've found that gal's body," he said. "You keep an eye on the president. She may ditch the potions in favor of a Tommy gun. It ain't as quiet, but it's a hell of a lot more effective. I need to find Bonnie."

The guards around Roosevelt were moving, forming a fortress of bodies next to him.

"Is there a doctor in the house?" someone yelled.

Clyde ran to the bar and saw a pair of white gloves in the trash, two empty glasses, and a little brown vial. He slipped it into his pocket and ran into the side room, scanning the surprised staff.

"Did a couple of gals come through here, maybe right behind each other?" he shouted, and one of the butlers tilted his head toward the servants' hallway.

He ran down the long hall, haunted by a familiar smell in the shadows—jasmine and rose and decaying lilies. It was the scent of the killer, the perfume Bonnie had sampled in the hotel room.

A door near the end of the hall was partially open, and he ran toward it, heart sinking when he saw a pair legs on the floor. His knees almost buckled as he willed himself to look—it wasn't Bonnie, but his relief was short-lived. Her little pearl-handled .25 was on the floor beside the corpse, along with a wooden lobster mallet, the end smeared with blood.

With an oath, he yanked his .45 out and ran toward a back door and threw it open, racing across the White House grounds to an exit. A block away down the darkened street, a car roared to life and gears ground. Clyde ran toward it, hollering at the top of his lungs for it to stop. The driver, a woman, stepped on the gas, and the car swerved out into the street, fishtailing.

Clyde fired into the rear window. The driver ducked as the glass shattered, and bullets whistled past. She chanced one nervous look back in his direction, her dark eyes set off by a flash of white, like a panicked race horse. Then she accelerated away and left him standing by the now-empty parking space and an overturned drink cart, smeared with a swipe of blood.

Cursing and panting, he slapped in a fresh clip and steadied his aim. Not sure if Bonnie was in the trunk or the back seat, he yelled in frustrated anger and emptied his gun straight up into the night sky.

CHAPTER 42

Good help is hard to find

The maid flipped on the electric lights and cracked open the balcony doors, letting in a cool breeze. They would be smoking soon—at least the two men—and those infernal cigars would fill the room with their oily haze. She swiped at the pedestal of a sculpture with her feather duster and then backed out, head bowed, shutting the heavy door behind her.

To the three barons, Emma was invisible.

They sat in the couches around the center of the room, already restored to its pre-explosion comfort. Ice sweat dripped from a bucket on the low-rise table in front of them, where champagne chilled. Stubbs let his attention wander upward to the spiderlike network of new cracks on the ceiling caused by the dynamite. He cracked his knuckles.

"Perhaps we should pop it now," Farquist said. "Bad news or good, champagne can only help."

"I agree," Dunthorpe said. "This waiting around is maudlin."

"By all means. Angela, do the honors," Stubbs said.

She uncrossed her legs and stood. "Because I'm a woman, you want me to serve?"

"I want you to serve because I am a large man who will undoubtedly have trouble extricating myself from this plush new couch," he said. "And also because I doubt young Farquist has the stamina to open one of these stubborn bottles."

Angela pulled the bottle out of the ice, made a show of popping the cork and letting the cascade of foam spill onto the carpet. She filled three glasses with the same reckless abandon, smiling pointedly at Stubbs as the liquid covered the table.

"You are in a petulant mood tonight," Stubbs said.

"The French claim the champagne glass was designed to mimic the perfect breast size, but I'd rather like mine larger," Farquist said.

"The glass or the breast?" Dunthorpe asked.

"Definitely the glass," he said.

"You're a pervert," she said. "But luckily I find that entertaining." She picked up her own glass and sat down again.

"Let's toast, shall we?" Farquist said. "To the working man. Long may he toil."

"How about instead we drink to success in our plan to stem the tide of misguided regulations and turn this country back onto the correct path, where those who understand wealth and success can make the decisions?" Dunthorpe said.

"Well, that's a rather wordy toast, but why not?" Farquist said, raising his glass.

"Here, here," Stubbs said.

Dunthorpe sipped the champagne without lifting her glass.

"Have a sense of humor, would you?" Farquist said, taking a drink. "Serious women are tiresome."

Stubbs pulled a cigar from his breast pocket and, after inspecting the edge of the clipper for any telltale remnants of blood or skin, clipped the tip and lit it with a great billowing of smoke. "There is no humor in the step we have been forced to take," he said.

Dunthorpe stood and opened the balcony doors wider. The smell of cigars sickened her.

"But one does what one must," Stubbs said, exhaling a long stream of blue smoke, pinching his face in a way that made his jowls prominent. "We cannot allow this great country to be destroyed. We are its protectors."

Dunthorpe sipped her champagne and did not answer.

"And we should never waste a crisis," Farquist said.

She watched a Hansom cab make its way down the street. Soon, she thought, automobiles will replace them all, and every American family will want one of their own. She imagined the factories that would be needed for this new invention, and the thousands of jobs her family would create.

"He should not have betrayed us, his own kind, with this misbegotten socialism nonsense," Dunthorpe said. "His belief that the government should protect workers will destroy the economy. A minimum wage? Regulating how many hours per day they can work, forcing businesses to contribute to their retirement? These financial decisions must remain in the hands of employers if this country is to flourish."

"I agree," Stubbs said. "Empowering labor to the degree he proposes imperils capital and thus threatens the health of this economy." He struggled to reach the champagne bottle, surging his frame forward but it was just out of reach.

Dunthorpe shook her head and walked over, picked up the bottle and handed it to him. "You're right, that was painful to watch."

"You are in a black mood tonight," Stubbs said, emptying the bottle into his glass.

"We'll need more bubbly," Farquist said. He was already two sheets to the wind, probably as good a state as any for such a momentous occasion. "Ring for the maid, would you?"

Instead, the phone on the table in front of them rang. They froze.

It rang again. Dunthorpe picked up the handset and handed it to Stubbs, listening to his side of the conversation.

"Yes."

"How?"

"Unacceptable."

"Bring her here."

He let the phone fall from his hands and then threw his flute against the wall, splintering champagne with shards of glass.

"Don't keep us in suspense," Farquist said.

"You are an idiot," Dunthorpe said, then turned her attention to Stubbs. "Is the president dead?"

He shook his head. "No. And worse, our employee was identified," Stubbs said.

"Must we flee?" Angela asked.

"I don't think so," Stubbs said. "We have leverage at this point. A hostage. One of the two people at the party who interrupted the assignment."

"There can be no witnesses—nothing tying us to this," Dunthorpe said. "Don't bring the killer here."

"We must," Stubbs said. "The meddlers can identify us. We will have to use the hostage to draw the other witness into our web."

"How?" Farquist asked. He was rattled now that events appeared to potentially have personal consequences.

"Our employee will bring the hostage here," he said.

"At which time we will devise our next steps." He looked at his watch. "It will be a reunion to remember."

"What do you mean?" Dunthorpe asked.

"The hostage—the woman who intervened and saved the president—is Brenda Prentiss," Stubbs said.

"You ancient idiot," she said, at a near whisper that cut deeper than any shout. "I told you to get rid of them. But no, you had to hire them."

"We underestimated the Texas trash," Farquist said.

"Do you think so?" Dunthorpe asked, sarcastically.

"That's not our biggest problem at the moment," Stubbs said.

"Of course not," Dunthorpe said. Farquist looked at her, puzzled. "The real question is who do the hillbillies work for?"

CHAPTER 43

Separated

The sun struggled to rise, spilling jagged fingers of light across the mall. Clyde was inconsolable and deranged, punching his fist into his thigh, again and again. "If something happens to Bon, I don't know what I'll do," he said. "I just don't know what I'll do."

Sal was scared for both of them. They sat on the white marble steps of the Lincoln Memorial, deserted at this hour, and she tried to slow his storm. "You have to calm down," she said, resting her hand on his arm.

He looked at her with pain-glazed eyes. "I don't know what I'll do."

"We'll find her. I've got my people looking."

"That woman was seconds away from killing the president," Clyde said. "Of the United States." He was stunned as the magnitude of everything from the last week began to really sink in.

"Yeah, and you stopped her. You figured it out."

"Aww, no, it wasn't me. It was Bonnie," he moaned. "She figured it out. She's the one who done it all and now I let her down, and she's gonna end up in a ditch somewhere like one of them mice."

Sal slapped his cheek hard, jarring his head to the side and splitting his lip at the corner. "Barrow, get a hold of yourself."

Shock flared through his eyes. He pulled a handkerchief from his vest pocket and dabbed the blood from the split. "You ought not to ever hit me again, Sal." His voice was flat and certain, like a coal shovel.

She nodded, suddenly feeling alone and vulnerable, but it worked, getting him focused on the present.

"If you want to get her back, think about what we need to do next. What would Bonnie do?"

He sighed and shook his head. "She'd probably tell me to cut my losses and get out now."

"Would she mean it?"

"She'd think she meant it. But she'd know I couldn't." He took off his hat and ran his fingers through his short hair and stared at the reflecting pool, seeing only empty space and dark possibilities.

"That's what makes us so good together," he said. "She's the brains. She can think real deep about things and come up with plans. I'm the muscle. I'm the triggerman and the driver. She can puzzle out what needs to get done, and then I do it. I'm not used to this, having to think and plot."

"For her sake, let's hope you can learn on the fly," Sal said. "We need to figure out where the killer would go. Where would you go?"

"Sal, we were never criminal masterminds. We were just lucky and desperate."

"Then it's time to grow a little bit," she said. "For Bonnie's sake."

He closed his eyes and let his thoughts drift back in time from the White House to their days on the road and even further, to prison. "One time, this inmate was supposed to give me a beating, the disfiguring kind, on orders of one of the screws who didn't like my sass. Anyway, I seen it coming and walloped him in the head with a food tray. It kept him off my back, but the guard wanted to send a message, so he broke that poor bastard's leg in four places so everyone would see him coming and know."

"Not sure where you're going with this," Sal said.

"If I was the killer, after not hitting the mark, I might worry I have a bull's eye on my back now," Clyde said. "And worry them three barons would want to make an example of me."

"Three barons?"

"That's what Bonnie named them," Clyde said.

"Back to your story. What does it mean?"

"It means she's either gone to ground, and we'll never find her or Bonnie again," he said, the despair seeping back around the edge of his voice.

"It feels like there was an 'or' coming," Sal said.

"Or she'll try to trade Bonnie for her own life," he said. "Which means it's back to them three barons in New York."

He thought about the map in the Willard Hotel room where they found the dead mice.

"The killer had a backup plan in case things went to hell. She'd mapped out a couple of escape routes, and they all led toward Union Station," he said.

"We've got people watching all departing trains," Sal said.

"It wasn't exactly the train station, though," Clyde said. "I'm gonna to go grab the map and check it out. If you don't hear from me by tonight, it means she's gone, and I'm dead, and you have to get Bonnie away from them three assholes."

She nodded.

"You got to swear to me that you will get her out."

"I swear."

"Sal, you have to mean it. I will crawl right out of hell and drag you back with me if you let anything happen to her."

"I will leave for New York now," she said. "We only stopped the attempt, not the impetus for another. One way or the other, we have to take your three barons down."

An hour later, Clyde was driving toward Union Station with the map unfolded on the seat beside him. The escape routes the assassin mapped out led past the train station to a building on Massachusetts and Second.

The location was a fruit and vegetable wholesaler bustling with activity as crates of apples and bananas arrived from the train station and were parceled out into trucks for distribution to local grocers and restaurants.

Clyde parked out front, buttoned up his jacket to hide the pistols, and walked in the front door.

The place was buzzing with activity as the early morning produce shipments arrived, and no one paid him any special mind—not the workers stacking up boxes or the managers ticking off order forms. Only the coffee girl took notice, eyeing the rumpled suit and the swagger out of place in the warehouse. She was small, Bonnie's size, Clyde thought, and with short, blonde hair too.

She smiled and tucked a strand of hair behind her ear. "Coffee?" she asked. Her fingers were stained brown from coffee grounds.

"You bet," he said, and she filled a cup of coffee out of the urn.

"We've got donuts and ham sandwiches for lunch, real cheap. Maybe even free if you tell me your name."

"That's kind of you, darling," he said, taking a sip. "But if my gal found us mooning over each other, she'd skin us both alive."

"Not like she needs to know," the coffee girl said, but Clyde shook his head, and she saw he meant it. She made a flirtatious pout anyway.

"Which one of these fine fellows is in charge?" Clyde asked.

She pointed at a ruddy-faced man with a bristly mustache that looked stolen from a flat broom. "Come back if you change your mind about the sandwich," she said. "Or anything else."

He touched the brim of his fedora and walked past the loading docks and up to the floor boss. "Howdy."

The man looked him up and down. "We're not hiring. Especially not limping runts."

Clyde fought the urge to bust him in the mouth. "Good thing I ain't looking for work then," he said.

"Then why the hell are you on my loading dock? You got an order to place, you go to the office, like everyone else."

"Naw, it ain't like that," Clyde said. "I'm looking for my gal, and her, uh, friend."

"Son, I don't think you know what it is we do here. We sell fruits and vegetables, not peaches and tomatoes."

"Yeah, but the thing is, she said she was gonna meet me here today. She's real pretty—a cute little blonde, and her friend is a little older, tall, real tan looking—kind of a mean streak."

The floor boss crossed his arms. "I don't know if you're drunk or just stupid, but if you don't get out of my sight, I'm gonna have someone throw you out onto the street, and none too gentle."

"Fair enough," Clyde said. He turned to walk back along the busy loading docks. A truck was finishing loading up, and the man slammed the back shut, pounded on the door, and the engine revved up.

Mixed in with the smell of overripe apples, bananas,

and oranges, Clyde caught a whiff of something else. Something sickly sweet, like jasmine and roses—and dead lilies. It was that fancy new perfume again. The assassin was here.

He yelled for the truck to stop, but the man who had just loaded the last crates shouted a warning. The driver stepped on the gas, and the truck rumbled away from the dock and toward the open doors. Clyde saw dark, nervous eyes peering through the tiny window on the back of the truck. The assassin.

He ran toward it, but the dockworker stepped in front of him and pulled a gun from his belt—a little .38. Clyde was faster, jerking out his .45 and blasting away at him. The man dove behind a wall of boxes filled with cabbages as the big slugs blasted the heads into coleslaw, and the place erupted in chaos.

The coffee girl shrieked and tipped over her cart, running for the back door with her hands over her ears. The manager turned a deeper shade of red and was crabbing out of sight behind a solid wall of tomatoes. Most of the workers were running for their lives, but a few of them—those who had been handpicked by the owner, Archibald Farquist—ran toward him, some with guns, others with long sticks with curved spikes on the end for toppling over crates.

Clyde stood his ground, dropping the clip out his pistol for a fresh one, then pulled the second .45. With a gun in each hand, he began blasting at the approaching thugs methodically as he walked backward toward the front door. As his bullets found flesh, spinning men away with groans and curses, their resolve broke, and they ducked for cover.

Once he made it outside, Clyde sprinted for the car and pulled the BAR out of the back seat. As the remaining pursuers spilled out into the street, Clyde met them with a withering hail of high-caliber gunfire that sent them back inside the building.

"I'm coming, Bon," he hollered, jumping behind the wheel and roaring off after the truck, following it down Massachusetts Avenue. He almost caught it when it slowed to turn, but another driver cut him off, and he had to swerve wide and rattle up onto the sidewalk.

Cursing, he ground the car back into gear and raced after the truck.

It slowed again to make the turn onto Pennsylvania Avenue, and the driver leaned out and fired wildly at Clyde. The bullets slapped across the grill, and one shattered the glass.

"Not even close, you sons of bitches," Clyde yelled, flooring it. "I got you now!"

The driver ducked back in the cab of the fruit truck and accelerated toward the bridge over the Potomac River. Clyde matched their speed, grimly aiming his car at the rear of the truck.

He was so focused on the chance of saving Bonnie he didn't see a second fruit truck roaring up from behind. As Clyde sped onto the bridge, the second truck caught up with him and slammed into his bumper.

"Son of a bitch," Clyde said as the impact jolted him. With a groaning screech of metal, the truck rammed his car into the bridge guardrails. It tipped onto two wheels and then flipped and went tumbling end over end into the air until it hit the river with a splash that sprayed water up in a plume. With a belch of air bubbles, the car slipped out of sight under the water.

The driver of the first truck looked back and smiled, then sped off out of sight, bound for New York.

CHAPTER 44

Special delivery

Bonnie came to her senses in total darkness, jarred by the motion of highway travel.

Her hands were tied, her ankles bound, and a rough gag that smelled faintly of gasoline plugged her mouth. Memories of the White House party rushed back. A flare of panic arced through Bonnie, amplifying the ache in her head.

That bitch assassin.

Wherever she was smelled like spoiled orange juice and day-old onions. She called for Clyde, then remembered the cover and called for Clarence. Neither answered.

Bonnie shoved both feet out, and a wall of boxed oranges toppled forward. Light streamed in, and she squinted. She was in a fruit truck. A woman stepped over the spilled boxes and glared down at her. Bonnie struggled against the restraints and tried her best to fix the woman with an intimidating stare.

"The dress shop called and told me how nice my sister was to check in," she said. "Pity my sister died fifteen years ago under a British boot heel."

The woman pulled a vial from her pocket and poured a colorless liquid onto a scrap of cloth and reached it toward Bonnie's face.

Bonnie kicked and screamed, and the assassin smiled. "Don't worry, they want you alive, but your voice is grating. Better you sleep," she said, as she pushed the cloth over her captive's nose. Bonnie held her breath as long as she could, but it wasn't enough. The sharp, metallic smell sent her into forced unconsciousness.

The next thing she felt was a stinging slap across her cheek. She couldn't see and could barely breathe. A burlap bag was tight over her head. "Wake up," a female voice said, and then another slap. "Wake up, you dirt-eating hillbilly."

She knew the voice and felt the rage behind the ineffective slaps—Dunthorpe.

Bonnie's mouth was as dry as an old cotton field, and her arms and legs felt like cement.

"We need her alive, but just barely," Dunthorpe said. "Bring her inside."

"Okay, boss," a man said.

His voice was familiar too. She was picked up and thrown over a set of broad shoulders and then trudged down a set of stairs. Bonnie counted each footfall—seven down a staircase, thirty-eight across a flat stretch with a turn to the right, and then to the left, and eighteen more down another set of stairs.

A door creaked open, and the air rushing out was cold. "Cuff her to the wall," Dunthorpe said. "Lock up behind you."

The man set her down and untied her. He lifted her arms, and she felt metal around her wrists. The bracelets clicked into place. He handled her with surprising gentleness, turning to maximize her comfort and then pulling off the bag from her head.

"Eugene, how many chances do we have to give you?" she asked weakly.

"I'm real sorry about this, Mrs. Prentiss, but I have to make a living," he said. "I wish more than anything it had turned out differently."

"Me too, Eugene," she said. She looked around the room. "It's cold in here. Where am I?"

"I'm not supposed to say," he said. "But it's a wine cellar."

"I thought you weren't supposed to say."

"I didn't say where."

"It can only be at Stubbs's place. Is he sore we blew up his safe?"

Eugene nodded. "More so about whatever happened in DC," he said.

"He tried to kill the president," she said. "Did you know that? Him and the other two. They tried to kill the president of the United States, just so they can make a little more money."

"I wouldn't know anything about that," he said.

"Well, you should know more about it. Get yourself educated, Eugene. Let me go, and I'll prove it to you," she said, rattling her handcuffs.

"That wouldn't be a wise move for me," he said.

"You don't want Clarence to think you treated me poorly, do you?" she asked.

He looked at her sadly. "They haven't told you."

"Told me what?" she asked, and he took a stride back. "Told me what?"

"I'm real sorry," he said, then stepped out and closed the heavy door, bolting it securely.

"At least give me something to drink," she yelled at the door. "A glass of water or a corkscrew."

She heard him walk away, clumping up eighteen steps until the sound faded. Bonnie looked around the gloomy room, the dusty bottles just out of reach, and hoped

Clyde was on his way.

After leaving her, Eugene took up his position outside the upstairs drawing room where the three barons were in a heated discussion.

They were satisfied that Clarence Prentiss was filled with lead and soaking at the bottom of the Potomac River. The truck driver saw it all. But what they didn't know was who was pulling the strings of the white trash spies. Given enough time, they could torture it out of the woman, but for all they knew, an assault on their holdings was already in the works.

"I say we cut our losses, kill her, and then lay low until this blows over," Farquist said. "Take a trip to the continent."

"That's your answer to everything," Dunthorpe snarled. "In the meantime, our assets will be out of reach." She splashed some brandy into a cup of coffee. "How did these hillbillies figure out our plan?"

She glared at Stubbs and then Farquist, and when he puzzled through the weight of the question, Farquist joined her in staring at the older man.

"There was no explicit information about our plot in the safe," Stubbs said.

"My dear friend," Farquist said. "What was in the safe, then, and why did you risk your reputation by pursuing it so doggedly?"

"Ledgers, receipts, bills," he said. "Nothing explicit, as I said. And I don't like your tone. They stole from me, from us. That's enough."

"You were more concerned about the safe than the thousands they stole from the bank," Dunthorpe said. "Are you sure there wasn't anything interesting in the safe?"

"Absolutely not," Stubbs said. He was angry and ramrod stiff, slowly massaging the left side of his chest.

"Can we please focus on the problem at hand?"

Farquist flipped out the tails of his jacket before sitting down lightly in an easy chair. He pulled a tiny derringer out of his pocket and placed it on the end table in easy reach.

Dunthorpe arched an eyebrow.

"Challenging times," Farquist said. "Now tell me, what did our lovely, deadly émigré have to say?"

"She saw no one other than the hillbilly bumpkins," Dunthorpe said, refilling her cup with brandy only. Her hand trembled from anger.

"Bring her down," Stubbs said. "I want to question her myself."

"Fetch her yourself," Dunthorpe said. "I'm leaving. You know what needs to be done."

Stubbs walked up and pushed his face inches from her cheek—so close she could see the yellowing in his beard from cigars and could smell breakfast sardines on his breath. At this distance, his size was imposing, and she blanched, in spite of herself.

"You are not leaving. We are in this together now, to the bitter end," he said.

"Lady and gentleman, now is not the time to fall apart," Farquist said. "Remember who you are and what resources you command. We will find someone to take the fall, if needed, as was done with Zangara. Indeed, we are old hands at this by now." He chuckled, but there was nervous panic beneath his laugh. "But first, we must know who we are destroying."

Stubbs and Angela stepped back from one another. "What do you suggest?" Stubbs asked.

"I suggest we let our Russian employee use her special skills to pry information from the Texan woman," Farquist said. "When she breaks, we'll know who our fight is with."

"We know she's tough," Dunthorpe said. "What if she doesn't break?"

"We will hang the assassination attempt on the hillbillies, eliminate our assassin and wrap up two loose ends for the price of one."

Stubbs smiled broadly, while Dunthorpe nodded with admiration. "Archibald, I'd forgotten why we asked you to join this little club in the first place," she said.

CHAPTER 45

The first cut is not the deepest

Downstairs, Bonnie dreamed she was in her momma's root cellar as a tornado bore down on the house. She and her mother sat with their backs against the dirt walls, playing dominos. Her mother played the double five and looked at her expectantly. "Aren't you going to count my score?" her momma said. Dream Bonnie didn't move.

"You were always such a selfish little thing," her mother said, now holding a bible with a grimy, hard-used, white leather cover.

Before she could speak, a howling wind ripped the wooden door off its hinges, and Bonnie's mother was swept into the vortex, her lips pursed disapprovingly as she disappeared.

Bonnie woke with a start and looked around the wine cellar. She was used to the temperature, more or less, but she was stupid hungry and every time she moved, darkness pressed in around her eyes. If that assassin lady permanently ruined my eyesight with her potions, Bonnie thought, there was going to be a reckoning.

She was sure Clyde was coming for her, but knew she needed to find a way out on her own, in case he was delayed. She craned her neck to look above her, and the sudden motion caused her to black out again.

When Bonnie next woke, her head bobbing as she

tried to remain conscious, she swore to temper her movements. In the haze, she wondered if this was the end. Dying didn't scare her, not exactly. She always figured she and Clyde would die young. But she also figured they would go down together.

And then she realized that this crazy second chance at life that Sal had given them had sparked an unfamiliar feeling inside her—hope; hope beyond just not dying alone, hope that she might actually live a life of some usefulness, even meaning.

She thought about that woman she met at her own funeral—the widow of the policeman they killed. She remembered her husband's young face, how he looked at Bonnie and Clyde with equal parts pleading for life and daring them to shoot. Why had they always only responded to the brutal challenges thrown their way? There was no purpose in anything she and Clyde had ever done. They were like bats when the lights came on—bumping around, reacting, and flying wildly.

The door swung open and light from the hall flashed through the room. Bonnie was blinded and when her vision adjusted, her blood chilled like the wine in the fine bottles surrounding her. It was the assassin, and she held a straight razor.

"I will take no pleasure from this," she said.

"Then why does it seem like you're smiling?" Bonnie asked, scooting as far back against the wall as the cuffs allowed.

"We need answers," the woman said. "The quicker you tell me, and convince me of your honesty, the quicker we can go our separate ways."

"I get the feeling my way is going to be bleeding out in a basement."

"I need light," the woman said.

Eugene lumbered into the room and reached up to the ceiling, screwing in the overhead bulb.

"Eugene, this is your last chance," Bonnie said. "I won't be so forgiving next time."

"Tell her what she needs to hear, Mrs. Prentiss," he said.

"Wait outside, and be ready to clean up," the woman said.

Eugene smiled sorrowfully at Bonnie then pulled the massive door closed behind him. Bonnie could hear him whistling quietly, *Brother, Can You Spare a Dime*. She hated that song.

The woman stood over Bonnie, tapping the razor blade against her palm softly, unconsciously keeping time to Eugene's artless tune.

"Is your name really Ballantine?"

"Is your name really Prentiss?" She had a faint but unmistakable accent, but Bonnie wasn't sure from what country. She'd never heard anyone speak from a country other than America, except for in the movies.

"No."

In the harsh light of the swinging bulb, Bonnie finally got a good look at her. Pushing forty, tiny crow's feet around tired eyes, but pretty and terrifyingly confident. She was taller than Bonnie and heavier—muscle though, not fat; even if she were healthy and unchained, Bonnie wasn't sure she could take her in a fair fight. But what fight was ever fair?

Unlike at the bar from the night before, her black hair was loose, shoulder-length. No gloves this time, and her hands were big and weathered, with no wedding band. There was a faded scar slashed across her right cheek that she must have concealed with makeup earlier.

"You know it's only a matter of time," Bonnie said.

"Before what?" she asked.

"Before my man busts in here to save me," Bonnie said.

The woman arched on eyebrow. "Oh no, my precious little turnip, he won't be riding in on his white horse to rescue you," she said, her voice a balance of sadness and glee. "He's at the bottom of the Potomac River. What's the phrase? He's eating with the fishes."

Bonnie's heart cracked in half, and she felt the will to fight, to survive, seep out of her like air from a punctured tire. But no, she thought. She would not believe it.

"Don't write him off yet," she said. "He's a damn good swimmer. And it's sleeping with the fishes."

"English is such an impossible language," the woman said with a wave of her hand. "And anyway, most people who get shot lose their swimming skills quickly." She squatted close. "You and I have much to talk about." She used the tip of the straightedge to trace Bonnie's cheek lightly.

"Like why you tried to kill the president?" Bonnie asked, straining against the cuffs holding her hands behind her back and tightly to the wall. "What do you have against America?"

"Nothing," she said, truly surprised. "Nothing at all. A paid job. You and your dead lover messed it up for me, and now I have to make things right." She pressed the razor more firmly into Bonnie's cheek, but not enough to break the skin. "So here is what will happen," she said. "You will tell me who employs you, and once I have this information, I will make this quick."

"What makes you think I work for anyone?" Bonnie asked.

"Slow it is, then," she said, dragging the blade quickly and deeply across Bonnie's cheek.

Bonnie felt the skin and flesh part and a dribble of blood snaked its way into her mouth. She pulled her head back so hard it cracked against the wall.

The woman touched her own cheek and the scar there. "Now we are like twins," she said.

"You bitch," Bonnie railed. "When I get out of here—"

"You are not getting out of here," the assassin said. "I will get the answers. The only question is how much will you and I come to resemble each other. She stood and lifted her shirt, revealing a flat, dusky stomach crisscrossed with a patchwork of scars. "They go much lower, if you know what I mean."

Bonnie was speechless, but only for an instant. "You're like a monster in a movie. Where are you from, Mars?"

"I am from a future that no longer exists. I am from hell," she said.

"What do you know, I'm from Texas too," Bonnie said, with more bravado that she felt.

The woman leaned down close again and used the razor to tug up under the sleeves of Bonnie's dress and cut it away from her so that it slowly slid down, revealing her slip.

"Thanks, honey. That dress was always a little on the snug side," Bonnie said.

"From experience, I can tell you that the breasts—especially the nipples—are very sensitive to the razor. I'm not ashamed to tell you I screamed a lot when I learned that." She nicked the tops of both Bonnie's exposed shoulders, so blood began seeping down her arms, standing out against the pale white skin. "But we have some time. We'll save that for later." She paused. "By the way, the breasts aren't the worst. Not by a long shot."

"I'd like to stay alive," Bonnie said through gritted teeth. "You know, to learn from all this so I can be more like you."

"Your blundering has gotten us both into a big mess," she said. "I can't let you live."

"They'll kill you too," Bonnie said. "You have to know that, right?"

"Until the light is actually gone, there's always the possibility of survival," she said.

"Did you see his body?" Bonnie asked. "Did you see the light go?"

"Make this easy on us both. Who do you work for?" she asked.

"I don't know, exactly," Bonnie said. "But I know you've got skills they would find mighty useful. "That's how Clarence and I got recruited." Or kidnapped, she thought.

"You would say anything to save your life," the woman said.

Bonnie, sensing an opening, sat up straighter, ignoring the blood dripping down her cheek and the splatter on the tops of her breasts. "I have nothing personal against you, other than killing that poor bartender, but I've got a whole lot of anger for them assholes upstairs. We're doing their dirty work, fighting and killing and murdering, and they're drinking champagne and laughing at us."

The woman rocked back on her heels. Bonnie could not tell if she was listening.

"And they are going to kill you," Bonnie said. "Or let you take the fall for me. You'll be in the chair, just like Zangara, the last sap they hired. But we can pay you. A lot."

"Money is a poor substitute for honor," she said. "I can't take a chance like this until you tell me what you know."

Bonnie knew it was probably a con, but she was all out of angles. "I work for a lady called Sal, but that isn't her real name," Bonnie said. "She was at that fancy party last night, in a pink dress, a guest, so I know she's real

265

powerful, and I think she's one of the good guys, but I'm not entirely sure of that yet. If you get us out of here, I promise I will set you up to meet her."

"There is no way for us to get out of here," the assassin said. Her accent seemed thicker now, and she pulled down a bottle of wine, studied it closely, and Bonnie feared she was about to be bludgeoned to death. Instead, the woman smashed the neck off and tipped it up to fountain wine into her mouth. "A very good year," she said, offering it to Bonnie.

Bonnie nodded and the woman poured red wine into her mouth and down her chin and throat, mixing with the blood.

"My name is Marianne," the assassin said.

"I'm Bonnie, but I go by Brenda," she said. "Listen, I've got some bad stuff on those people upstairs—the ones that hired you. Stuff that's gonna hurt them—photos of them doing bad things, deviant things. We just have to get out of here."

"I was supposed to be on the Queen of Bermuda, heading into a new life right now," Marianne said. "Because of you, I'm sitting in a wet, rodent-infested wine cellar and not doing my job again. It was supposed to be my last job. For that alone, I should kill you."

"I can get you on that ship," Bonnie said. "Or at least in a job that has a better class of clients."

"If I agree, how would we accomplish that?"

"Well, we just have to—"

There was a heavy thud outside the door and then it swung open. Bonnie recognized Emma, the Negro maid from Texas. She was holding a fireplace poker, and Eugene lay unconscious at her feet.

The maid rifled through his pockets, pulled out a key and walked toward Bonnie, giving Marianne—who was still holding the razor—a wide berth. She bent and unlocked Bonnie's handcuffs.

"Do you work for Sal?" Bonnie asked, rubbing her wrists.

"Don't know no Sal," Emma said.

"Then why are you helping me?"

"Because when you're at the bottom together, you ought to stick together." Emma gave Marianne a sideways look. "No matter what country you call home."

Eugene groaned and his legs twitched.

"Plus, I don't really care much for those three bosses, and I think you might give them what they deserve. Now get going. You don't have much time. At the far end of this floor there's an old servant's stairwell leading to the back alley."

Emma turned and dashed back up the stairs.

Bonnie stood and fought against vertigo, taking in the tatters of her dress collapsed around her feet. She stepped out of the fabric and, now barefoot and clothed only in her blood- and wine-soaked slip, looked at Marianne hopefully. "Work together?"

The assassin weighed the paths opening before her, playing out the possible outcomes, and then reached her decision. "Fine, let's go," she said. "But first, someone has to die."

She reached toward Eugene with the razor in her hand, eyeing his throat.

"Wait…" Bonnie said, catching Marianne by the wrist. "I kind of have a soft spot for him."

The assassin glared at her and shook her arm free. "The man who left you with me to die?"

"He was just trying to get by," Bonnie said. As Eugene struggled back toward consciousness, Bonnie pulled his handkerchief out of the breast pocket of his suit and stuffed it into his mouth and then walked into the wine cellar to retrieve the handcuffs.

When she returned, Marianne was holding Eugene's .38 pointed casually toward her.

She ignored the threat and shackled Eugene's hands behind his back, locking him to a cellar radiator. "You got more lives than an old tom cat," Bonnie whispered. She pointed at Marianne. "She wanted to kill you, and I had to think real hard to come up with a reason to talk her out of it. I want you to remember just how close you came to dying every time you messed with me and Clarence."

He nodded, but his eyes were still unfocused.

"Let's get out of here," Bonnie said.

Marianne handed Eugene's gun to Bonnie. "Lead on. I am not very good with guns."

Bonnie checked the chamber to make sure it was loaded and mouthed a prayer that Clyde was alive and either on his way to her, or already on the run and planning his revenge when her escape from the heavily guarded mansion, with a duplicitous assassin at her side, inevitably failed.

CHAPTER 46

Trapped like rats

The servant stairwell was filled with cobwebs that stretched across her face as they slowly made their way through the darkness. Rats, surprised and disturbed by the passage of humans, scurried behind the walls and along the beams. Marianne swore softly when her elbow cracked into an angled joint of pipe.

Bonnie got down on her hands and knees and slowly moved forward, one hand in front, the darkness obscuring her path. Marianne followed suit.

The concrete floor was rough, and she occasionally felt puddles of oily, viscous fluid. Bonnie shuddered, not wanting to know what she was splashing through.

"I saw a little door when I came in the back earlier. We can't be too far from it, maybe ten meters," Marianne whispered.

"What is a meter?" Bonnie asked.

"Americans. Keep going. We're almost there."

Bonnie heard traffic and a bird singing. A mourning dove? Sing, she thought. Guide us out of here.

They scraped and pulled their way along the hallway, Bonnie reaching out into the shadows until her fingers came to a wall. She fluttered her hand over the surface until she felt hinges, then a heavy metal latch. Not a wall—the door. And on the other side, mourning doves,

New York, freedom, and certainty about Clyde.

"We're here," she said, her voice flooded with relief. "Get ready," she said, extending Eugene's gun and pulling on the latch. It didn't budge. She put the gun down and used both hands, but the latch held.

"Why would that colored girl waste all our time just to send us to a dead-end? Unless it was a test of my loyalty, and there's a trap waiting on the other side," Marianne said, pushing up beside her.

"I'm not crawling through that bullshit again," Bonnie said. "Help me pull."

Together the two women gripped the knob, their hands encircling it and each other, planting their feet against the stairs for leverage. Bonnie winced when Marianne stepped on her bare foot, but used the pain to pull harder.

Finally, the rusty mechanism started to give.

"Slowly, no noise," Marianne whispered.

The latch clicked, and they pushed their shoulder into the door, and it cracked open into the back garden, enclosed by a low brick wall covered with ivy, and shielded by a row of early summer rose buds.

Bonnie picked up the gun, and they made for the wall. Her heart was pounding. She was acutely aware of cool grass against her bare feet. With less than ten yards between them and freedom, a familiar voice cut through the evening air.

"My goodness, you look a fright," Dunthorpe said.

Bonnie spun and brought the pistol up, but she was outgunned. The three barons stood behind a wall of thugs, armed with an assortment of shotguns and Tommy guns aimed in their direction. One in the front was holding the maid by the hair with a gun to her head, her left eye swollen shut from vicious treatment.

Why, Bonnie thought—why is it always so damn hard?

"Mrs. Prentiss, I hope you know she dies first. Then you. Then…probably you, Miss Ballantine, unless you have a very convincing story for us," Stubbs said.

"I discovered who she works for," Marianne said. "I have done my job."

"You bitch," Bonnie said, cocking the gun and turning it toward Marianne.

Marianne slapped it out of her hand and faced Stubbs.

"I won't tell you until I am guaranteed safe passage."

"Bring them to the library," Stubbs said. "We'll sort out fact from fiction and settle our accounts there. Permanently."

CHAPTER 47

A grand entrance

Bonnie and Marianne were tied back-to-back by the fireplace in the library, their wrists bound awkwardly behind them like bent spring tree limbs. The maid huddled in the corner by the almost concealed servant's doorway, wiping blood from her mouth. The three barons were drinking brandy from a crystal decanter and arguing.

"We sent her to extract information," Stubbs said. "She says she has it. What is the harm in letting a foreign agent escape with her life?" He drained his glass and reached for the decanter.

"She knows too much about us," Dunthorpe said. "She was trying to escape." She took a nervous sip of the brandy.

"Which means she's rational," Farquist said, refilling his glass. "We were going to kill her no matter what, which I still support."

"This is not a democracy," Stubbs said. "We're not voting on this. I have more wealth than the two of you combined. What I say goes. I want to know who the hillbilly bumpkin works for."

"You are an arrogant son of a—" Dunthorpe started to say when a tremendous crash rattled the house. The three barons looked at one another with a slow kind of panic rising in their eyes.

"My man knows how to make an entrance," Bonnie said, laughing. "I'll never forget the day I first laid eyes on him, strutting around with enough confidence for two men. Two big men," she said, eyeing Farquist and Stubbs. "Bigger than you, that's for sure."

Stubbs took a step toward Marianne, raising his cane. "Tell me who they work for," he said.

"I have no idea," she said, and then looked sadly at Bonnie. "There is always hope until the light dies."

His angry attention was diverted by a hasty knock on the door, and Stubbs spun and unsheathed a sword from the cane while Farquist pulled out his tiny derringer.

But it was one of their thugs. "A car crashed into the house," he said. "There was no one in it, just a brick on the accelerator. Someone is making a run at us. Stay inside."

Stubbs nodded.

"Yes, by all means, stay inside," Bonnie said. "I'd hate for you all to fly away before he gets here with his BAR. Once he gets the shooting fever all worked up, there's no stopping him until he's either out of bullets or bodies."

"Then maybe I should just kill you now," Stubbs said, stepping toward her with the sword cane aimed at her heart, and smiling.

But the smile died from his face when a burst of automatic rifle fire chewed across the room, causing them all to dive for cover. Clyde stepped in from the servant's entrance.

At the sight of him, Bonnie felt her broken heart knit itself back together.

"I knew it," she whispered. "I knew you were still alive."

He smiled at her, keeping eye contact so long it seemed he had forgotten what he was doing. After a few long seconds of shared relief, he swapped out clips in his BAR and pointed at Stubbs, a curl of smoke wisping from the barrel. "Drop your pig-sticker."

Stubbs dropped the sword cane and stepped back.

Clyde helped the maid to her feet. "You look like you've had a long day. Why don't you knock off early?" he said. Emma slipped through the doorway and was gone.

The sound of gunfire from outside filtered in, sporadic, followed by long bursts from inside the house. "I brought the cavalry," Clyde said, walking into the room, the BAR at his waist and aimed toward the three barons, who were frozen in fear. Farquist held his little gun, but Clyde paid it no mind. He picked up the sword cane with his left hand and used it to slice through the ropes around Bonnie's wrists, freeing both her and Marianne, and then tossed it aside.

Bonnie stood, and he looked her up and down, relieved she was alive but concerned about the cuts and bruises and bloodied clothes and bare feet. "You okay?" he asked.

She threw herself into his free arm and kissed him so hard, they both saw stars. "I am now," she said. "Oh baby, I knew you weren't dead."

"It'd take more than a couple of dandies and a washed-up flapper to kill me," he said.

Bonnie disentangled herself from his embrace and slid one of his .45s out of the shoulder holster, cocked the hammer and aimed it at Dunthorpe. "I'm going to kill that one for trying, though," she said.

"We were told your car hit the water hard," Dunthorpe said.

"Ain't the first time I've gone off a bridge," he said. "The secret is relaxing a little, and making sure the steering wheel don't crush your chest."

"Our men waited for you to surface," Stubbs said.

"I've held my breath longer than that gigging for catfish," Clyde said. He looked at Marianne curiously, noticing how she never strayed from Bonnie's side. "Seems like you made a new friend, darling."

"Oh yeah," Bonnie said. "This is Marianne. She's real nice when she isn't cutting on you or trying to poison the president. Marianne, this here is, uh, Clarence."

Marianne nodded. "It's okay. Marianne isn't my real name, either."

"Whatever your name is, I'm glad you're on our side now," he said. "Poison gives me the heebie jeebies. Them dead mice in your hotel room—three of them in a little cage. I keep thinking about them."

"You can't possibly think you'll escape from here," Stubbs said. "As soon as our guards tidy up whatever little diversion you created, they'll surround this room. What other body parts are you willing to part with in exchange for your freedom?"

"We're not gonna escape," Clyde said. "We're gonna walk out of your front door like regular folk."

"And how's that?" Dunthorpe asked.

"Y'all don't know it yet, but you're already dead."

"What are you talking about?" Stubbs asked.

"That expensive hooch you've been swilling. I took the liberty of poisoning it with one of Marianne's special concoctions not more than an hour ago when I snuck in here while y'all were outside having your little garden party."

They looked at the glasses they were holding and then at the slim remainder of brandy in the decanter. As if choreographed, each dropped their glass, acting like the tumblers had suddenly grown red hot.

"That's right. I stopped by the black widow's lair

before I left our nation's capital and picked up a bottle of her finest poison. I spiked your drinks. I knew you sure as shit wouldn't be sharing it with Brenda." He looked at his watch. "Way I figure it, you'll be dead in about twenty minutes to an hour. That sound about right, Marianne?"

She was confused, knowing any of her poisons would have killed them almost instantly, but Bonnie gave her a little unseen nudge to help sell the lie. "That seems a little slow," Marianne said. "The brandy may have diluted the poison. But it will certainly be fatal."

"I'm surprised you ain't feeling a little flushed already—a little dizzy, maybe?" Clyde said.

Dunthorpe held her hand to her throat. "It is getting hot in here."

Farquist looked as if he was about to vomit. Beads of sweat appeared on his broad forehead. Stubbs clenched his jaw and glared.

"Yep, you're all gonna die," Clyde said. "Unless..." His voice trailed off.

"Unless what?" Stubbs asked.

"Unless you have the remedy," Clyde said. He pulled a small brown bottle from his vest pocket.

The last time Bonnie saw it, that same bottle was resting on a pillow to make sure the nitroglycerine inside didn't explode. The cavalier way he tossed it up and down, to emphasize his point, caught her breath in her throat.

"Help me out, Marianne. Think there's enough antidote in here to save one life?"

"Barely," she said, her face solemn. "But just one life."

"I will pay you ten thousand dollars for that bottle," Farquist said.

"I will double it," Dunthorpe said, trying to smile and reaching out her hand.

"One hundred thousand dollars plus safe passage," Stubbs thundered.

"You'll forgive me if I don't trust you all much right now," Clyde said. "What was it you said earlier? Something about having me over the barrel and you owning the barrel? Well now I own the barrel. And your money ain't worth much to me."

"I underestimated you," Stubbs said. "We all did."

"You underestimated this country," Clyde said. "What the hell is wrong with you people?"

"Short-sighted, I can see that now," Stubbs said, hoping to bring Clyde around to handing over the antidote. "But you must know that our intentions are noble. We want to be sure there are jobs for everyone. People like us, the ones who are good at making money—we are the best positioned to help others like you climb the ladder, not the government."

"I ain't never seen evidence of that ladder you're talking about," Clyde said. "Seems like mostly pretty words covering up a big old con you fat cats are running on the working man."

"Yea, you big money clowns broke the country in the first place and then expect us to believe you're the ones to fix it?" Bonnie added. "That's like putting a fox in charge of the henhouse after he already ate all the chickens."

"It takes time, and it's complicated," Stubbs said. "We will get the system fine-tuned so money can be made by everyone, good paying jobs can be had by all. You just have to be patient."

"That's what they told my daddy, and his daddy too," Clyde said. "I don't think you have a plan, just a sickness. You thinking you can do whatever you want to people just because you can lord your money over them, all the while telling them to be patient with no intention of changing a damn thing."

"Untrue," Stubbs said. "A very unfair characterization. Please sit down, and I'll explain it all to you."

"Yea, right. Now go on and remind me, what was that other thing you said to us before?" Bonnie asked. "Oh yea, that it was your country and you just let us work here? Well, it's our country, mister. We're the ones doing all the work but you're getting all the dough."

Clyde looked at her and grinned. "We're not really doing any work, baby, we're just doing the bank robbing," he said.

She shushed him with a look. "Well, maybe we aren't specifically doing the work, but all them good farmers and factory men and restaurant workers and coal miners, they're doing the work, and making you rich in the process, and they can barely scrape by on the peanuts you're giving them."

Clyde nodded. "I don't know why sharing the fruits of the working man's labor is so damn hard for you folks. Only way to do it is to force you, I guess. Now go stand at the far end of the room. I'll leave the antidote up on the top shelf here and when we shut the door—well, you can figure out who lives and who dies."

The three barons looked at one another nervously.

"Let's make it fair, though," he said. "Toss your little toy heater into the middle of the room here," he said to Farquist. When he complied, Clyde kicked the sword cane beside the tiny derringer and used the barrel of his gun to motion them to move. They huddled against the far wall.

"Let's go, Cly...Clarence," Bonnie said. When she opened the door, she ran into a dense wall of thugs aiming pistols, shotguns, and Tommy guns in their direction. Clyde whistled appreciatively at the array of guns. "Stubbs, you'd better call your dogs off or I just might drop this here antidote."

"Put your guns down," Stubbs ordered. "Let them pass."

Confused, the men did just that, letting the arsenal clatter to the ground. Marianne helped herself to a shotgun and tucked a .38 into her waistband.

"I thought you didn't care much for guns," Bonnie said.

"I am adaptable," she said.

"Good luck," Clyde said to the three barons, setting the bottle of nitroglycerine on the edge of the shelf.

"Rot in hell," Bonnie added, pulling the door closed and locking it.

Inside, they could hear screams and shouts and bodies colliding, and the pop pop of the derringer. The thugs looked around uncertainly, but let them pass.

"We should hurry," Clyde said. "Before they knock that nitro off the shelf."

By the time they got to the front door, an explosion rumbled through the building, belching smoke out the basement windows.

They joined the onlookers drawn to the commotion.

"Where's the cavalry?" Bonnie asked.

"There wasn't nobody but Sal and that man mountain that follows her around," Clyde said. "I saw them three assholes leading you back in from the garden, so I had them drive the car into the wall and distract the guards long enough for me to slip inside."

"That fake poison gag was pure gold," Bonnie said. She took his hand in hers and squeezed. "I was so worried about you, baby."

"Don't you ever leave my side again," he said, slipping off his jacket to cover her against the night air.

CHAPTER 48

No rest for the wicked

During the two days and nights that passed since they escaped from the barons, Bonnie and Clyde followed a pretty simple routine: they slept, made love, ate and drank too much, then started the whole cycle over again.

At first, the telephone rang off the hook, but Clyde yanked the cord from the wall socket, and then it was blissfully silent. They kept the drapes pulled tight so there was no way to feel the passage of time, only the softness and longing of their naked bodies entwined.

But on the third day, Bonnie rose from the bed and threw open the drapes. With the morning sun creating a halo around her head, to Clyde she looked like a Hollywood goddess, but one who was cruelly depriving him of his darkness.

"Come back to bed, Bon," Clyde said, squinting into the light and then covering his face with a pillow.

She shook out a cigarette and looked down at the Manhattan Street, bustling with cabs, trucks, and people.

"I love you, Clyde Barrow," Bonnie said.

"I love you too, Bonnie Parker," he said. "I'd like to love you again right now, in fact."

"It's time to meet her," she said.

"Do we have to?" Clyde groaned.

"Yep," she said with a nod. "We need to figure out

what comes next. We can't just hide out in this hotel room forever."

"Are you sure about that?" he asked. "Maybe just for a week or two?"

"Sal knows we're here," she said. "Pretty soon, she'll roust us, and I'd rather meet on neutral territory this time."

She plugged the phone in, and it rang almost immediately.

An hour later they walked into the Red Flame coffee shop, a few doors down from the hotel. Sal sat at a booth in the far corner, reading a newspaper. Bonnie and Clyde slid into the booth across from her. The electric fan in the corner buzzed like a tired hive of bees. A sad little girl sat at the table next to them, dressed in her Sunday finest. Bonnie wondered where her momma was taking her on a Thursday.

Sal lifted her head from the financial pages and winced. "You both look like hell," she said.

Clyde's face was battered from the car wreck and makeup couldn't hide the livid slit across Bonnie's cheek. Sal pushed the newspaper in front of them. "See this?"

Bonnie and Clyde looked at the article. A wet coffee ring circled part of the headline: *Banker found dead, assets seized due to criminal enterprises.*

"That Stubbs?" Clyde asked.

"Yes. His bank is closing."

"Why?"

"When Stubbs was killed, federal agents, along with their other less unsavory business partners, took a closer look at the books. Seems he had his hand in a number of illegal activities."

"Like trying to kill the president and bleed the working man to death?" Bonnie asked.

"That probably wouldn't be enough to close it, sadly, but he made some poor investment decisions, and that was the kiss of death to his silent investors," Sal said. "His bank was deeply leveraged. He was counting on opportunities from the New Deal falling apart, and there was no way back out of the swamp now."

"Silent investors?"

"Not all capitalists are bad. The vast majority are, in fact, quite necessary and in some cases exceptionally generous. Our job is to weed out the bad apples and protect the checks and balances so everyone gets a fair shake," Sal said.

The waitress stopped at the table, her order pad held high. "Just two coffees," Bonnie said. "We won't be staying."

"What about Farquist?" Clyde asked after the waitress left.

"He was disfigured by the explosion. He's recuperating in England, and given his documented sexual appetites—thanks for that—he won't be allowed to return."

"Dunthorpe?" Bonnie asked.

"She was unharmed by the blast, but took a bullet in the knee during the scuffle. We shared the pictures from the safe with her, and she decided to permanently relocate to France."

"Who was the man she was with?" Bonnie asked.

"That's classified," Sal said.

The waitress placed coffee cups on the table and refilled Sal's cup. Steam curled out and Sal added milk.

"So Dunthorpe skates?" Bonnie asked.

"We consider her fleeing the country a broken woman to be a partial but adequate success," Sal said.

"That isn't success in my book," Bonnie said. "I told that woman I'd come after her, and I aim to keep my word."

"You will do no such thing," Sal said. "Your first assignment is over. You performed reasonably well, and because of that, you remain alive, and your family will be unharmed."

"Performed reasonably well?" Clyde said. He backhanded the hot coffee cups onto the restaurant floor and then leaned on the table, his face inches from hers. "We saved the president, rescued the goddamn country, and nearly got killed in the process."

"Lower your voice, Prentiss," Sal said. "You're agents now. Act like it."

A busboy hurried over and knelt near the table, wiping up the spilled coffee. "Thanks, kid," Clyde said, slipping him a dollar bill. "Sorry about that. Don't ever let your temper get the better of you."

"You pulled me in when you needed help to attack Stubbs's mansion," Sal said to Clyde. "That was risky."

Clyde frowned, still irritated. "You and Carl did a pretty good job creating a diversion. After you crashed the car into the mansion, it sounded like a whole damn cavalry shooting at the barons," Clyde said. "Maybe you should be the spy rather than the boss?"

"I don't want to ever do that again," Sal said. "That risk was almost enough to offset your success."

Managing them in the future would be harder if they had big heads, Sal knew. Anger was almost always a better motivator than praise.

Clyde scowled and Bonnie thought about going for the gun in her garter and putting a slug right in her smug mug.

"Calm down, both of you," Sal said. "That you are still sitting here after running up a ridiculous room service bill and not rotting in some Mexican jail or dead in a swamp should be thanks enough for what you did."

"Thanks?" Bonnie asked incredulously. "You ruined our lives."

"Oh no," Sal said. "You took care of that all on your own. And ruined a lot of other lives in the process. You should be thanking me. How many people get a second chance in life, a shot at redemption?"

Sal took a sip of her coffee. "Oh, by the way, thanks for putting us in touch with Marianne. She does indeed have useful skills."

"Was the maid your eyes on the inside?" Clyde asked.

"Also classified," Sal said.

"Couldn't be anyone else. Had to be Emma," Bonnie said.

Sal stood. "There's a car outside with the keys under the seat. Take a break, a little vacation. Here, your funds are replenished. Every two weeks, call me at this number. Don't make me come find you."

Sal slid an envelope across the table and walked out.

They sipped the coffee in silence for a while. "I guess we're a gang of two now," Bonnie said finally, stirring two cubes of sugar into the cup without looking up at him. She watched the sugar dissolve into the liquid, losing its form.

"You don't sound too happy about that," Clyde said.

"Are you happy? I mean, never seeing our family again, not knowing who we work for, not knowing if they're bad or good?"

He clinked his coffee cup against hers. "The only time I know for sure that I'm happy is when I'm with you," he said.

Her eyes teared up a little. "I guess there are no easy answers."

"Who wants easy?" Clyde asked.

"Probably we were fighting against the wrong things before, robbing those little stores and banks," she said.

"And all it took to redeem our wicked ways was saving

the country," Clyde said, hoping his forced swagger would keep her darkening mood from going farther down a rabbit hole.

"We did make a difference," she said with a smile. "And we can keep doing it, but there's something else we've got to do first."

CHAPTER 49

Benevolence

A week later, Clyde stopped the car in front of a small wood-frame house, the last one on a dusty street on the outskirts of town. The lawn was overgrown, and a chicken pecked at the grass in the front of the house. A lone, rusty pump jack seesawed like a metronome behind the house.

"You sure this is it?" Clyde asked.

"I'm sure," Bonnie said.

"It's a risk to go in together," he said.

"Doesn't matter. No one would ever believe her anyway," Bonnie said.

Holding hands, they walked down the stone pathway to the house. Bonnie knocked on the door. A little boy about three or four years old answered. His pants were torn at the knee, and what looked like strawberry jam was smeared across his cheek. Bonnie licked her thumb and wiped the sticky substance off the boy's face.

"Boy, is your momma home?" Clyde asked.

"Momma, strangers to see you." He ran off shyly.

Clyde looked past the child at the living room area. The paint was peeling, and he caught a whiff of what smelled like burned toast. There was a couch and table but no other furniture. Probably selling things off one by one to make it, Clyde thought. He remembered that slow, painful process of becoming homeless, when nothing but a miracle would stop it, and the miracle never arrived.

A woman came in from the back room, her waist wrapped in an apron and her hair in pin curls. When she got closer, Bonnie noticed the dusty look of her complexion. The fire in her eyes, fueled by rage that Bonnie had seen just a few weeks before at her own funeral, had dimmed. Now, the woman looked worn-out and sad.

"Don't got a need for anything you're selling," she said. "And no money anyway." She pushed the little boy behind her, and he held onto her leg, peaking out curiously from behind.

"Wait," she said. "I recognize you. From that whore's funeral."

"Yes ma'am," Bonnie said. "We're here from the Parker Barrow Benevolence Fund."

"The what fund?" She pulled the pins from her hair and straightened it.

"The family of them two murderers raised some money to help the victims. And people are donating to it to help those affected," Clyde said.

She looked at him suspiciously. "Are you pulling my leg?"

"No ma'am," Bonnie said, handing her an envelope.

She opened it and thumbed through a stack of bills. "Is this from the police? The police said they would help me out, but then no one ever came around."

"It damn sure ain't from the police," Clyde said.

The woman looked up at them. "They killed my husband and left me a widow and single mother."

"Yes ma'am," Clyde said. "They were confused people who made some bad choices, but they come from a good family, and that's who wants to help now."

"Your husband was a good man, like most law officers, and we should all be grateful for their service," Bonnie said.

"This don't make no sense," the woman said, torn by the ramifications of the opportunity. "Is this from their stolen money?"

"No, ma'am, it's legal. And no one is ever going to come after it. But you might be well served to use it sparingly, so as not to call attention to your good fortune," Clyde said.

The widow fingered the bills, counting them. "There's near five hundred dollars here," she whispered.

And then the moment got the better of her, and she buckled and burst into tears, lifting her apron to cover her face. Bonnie knew she was crying both from anger and relief.

"Momma, what's wrong?" the boy asked. He began to cry too.

"You look after your momma, boy," he said. "We best be on our way."

The woman fanned herself and trying to control her emotions. "Wait, where are my manners. Please come in for some sweet tea," she said.

Bonnie smiled. "No, ma'am, but thank you."

They turned and walked back to the car.

"I'm real tore up about what happened to her husband," Clyde said, turning the key in the ignition. "But that felt good." He gunned the accelerator, and they sped away as if from a robbery.

"Yeah," she said.

"Why wasn't it the Barrow Parker Benevolence Fund? Why was your name first?" he asked.

She laughed. "Oh honey, everybody knows it's Bonnie and Clyde, not Clyde and Bonnie."

Clyde turned on the car radio. They listened to Bing Crosby singing about a million-dollar baby. Bonnie hummed along with the melody, and Clyde tapped out the rhythm on the steering wheel. Then the music abruptly stopped with a newsflash.

We interrupt this program to report the breaking news that John Dillinger has been shot by federal agents Melvin Purvis and Samuel Cowley in a bloody battle as he was leaving the Biograph Theater in Chicago today. Details to follow.

The radio flipped back to music.

"Think that means Sal has someone new for our gang?" Bonnie asked.

"Hope not," Clyde said. "Never did like that bastard."

"Yeah, I'm partial to it being just you and me from here on out," Bonnie said.

They rode in silence for a few minutes.

"Where to?" Bonnie asked.

"I'm a man of my word," he said. "And that means we've got a long drive ahead of us. We're going to visit the Empire State Building."

Her eyes lit up, and she clapped her hands. "But we just left New York," she said.

"Being in a car with you is the closest thing to heaven I can think of," Clyde said, pushing his fedora back.

She leaned over and pecked him on the cheek and then pulled out the map and started tracing the roads that would lead them north. "Let's take the scenic route."

CHAPTER 50

Old photographs

Bonnie placed a bunch of daisies next to the stone marking her mother's grave. She brushed off weeds and dirt from the plaque. A few feet from Emma Parker's grave was another plaque, also flush with the hard ground, marking Bonnie Parker's grave.

The site was well visited and trampled down from the curious. From earlier trips, Royce had learned that at least a few tourists and history buffs made the trek here every day to see the grave.

Royce stood a few feet behind, in the shade of an old elm tree, trying to be patient. He looked at his watch. A camera in a leather case hung around his neck.

Working well into the night, yesterday Royce had wrapped up the first article—three thousand words about Bonnie's incredible tale—and he was ready to share the story with his editor. He was tired but excited to finally tell his boss what had kept him away from work so much.

But more than that, Royce had begun dreaming. This was big, really big. Cautiously, he was thinking about awards and movie contracts.

The meeting with his editor was set for tomorrow morning. He wanted to be sure he made a real splash. He decided a photo was needed. Bonnie agreed, but was unwilling to change her regular weekly plan. He drove down to Dallas to meet her at Crown Hill Memorial Park.

After what seemed like way too long to Royce, Bonnie finally turned around. "Momma died ten years after me and Clyde got kidnapped by Sal and her lackeys," Bonnie said. "I never saw her again."

"That must have been hard."

Royce absently looked at his watch again, and when he glanced up, he saw that Bonnie was staring at him with an odd expression. "Did you call or write?" he asked, trying to be more politely attentive.

"I wrote a lot of letters I never mailed. And every now and again, I telephoned just to hear her voice. Once, in the silence, she said, 'Bonnie, is that you?' Like she knew, you know, that I was still alive. But that ended up making trouble for us."

"What kind of trouble?"

"That's a story for another day," Bonnie said.

"Why isn't Clyde buried here?" Royce asked.

"You'd have to ask his family that," she said. "But we both know the real Clyde is buried somewhere else entirely, and that isn't me down in that coffin next to my momma here."

"Your momma went to her grave thinking she was going to rest eternally next to you," Royce said.

Bonnie's shoulders slumped a little. But then she straightened up quickly. "I've made arrangements in my will to have her moved, after all this comes out."

Royce wondered if that was something that might fall to him to carry out someday. He thought about what he hoped was going to be a very public and well-paying future after this story broke, and figured that was the least he could do.

"Take a photo of me standing next to my momma's grave plaque?" she asked.

"Sure thing," he said.

Royce pulled the Nikon out of its case and walked out from under the shade of the tree. The midday sun threw shadows across the stone, and Royce repositioned her several times to get a good shot. She was comfortable being photographed, but never smiled, her hands gripping tightly to the handle of her beaded purse.

"That'll do," she said.

"That should do for my purposes too," he said. He began to put the camera away.

Bonnie opened her purse. She snapped open a compact, powdered her face, and then applied red lipstick.

Unbuttoning the coat, she let it drop to the dry, grassy ground. She was dressed in a striped shirt with a petite black shoulder sweater, a knee-length woolen skirt, nude stockings, and tan shoes with an ankle strap. She unfolded a hat that she pulled out her handbag and placed it on her head, tucking her hair beneath it, positioning the black felt beret so it hung a little farther over her left ear. Tucked beneath her arm was a holstered pistol.

When she walked closer to Royce, he smelled mothballs and noticed a dark stain on the left side of the skirt.

"You recognize this outfit?" she asked.

"Is that what you were wearing in—"

"I am pleased it fits," she said. "Guess I still got the body of a twenty-year-old."

When she laughed, the creases around her eyes bunched up.

"All right now, you want a real photo?" She walked over to her Cadillac. Bonnie placed her hand on her hip and leaned into the front trunk. "Oh wait, one more thing."

She crawled in the front seat and pulled something from the glove compartment. "Clyde isn't here so we can't recreate that photo exactly, and this car is not the same, but I know how we can improve this shot."

With a flourish, she placed a fat, brown cigar between her withered ruby lips and resumed her jaunty pose. Royce smiled and felt a rush of affection for the old woman. He snapped a bunch of photos, some with a flash, some without. He moved around to get the shot from different angles and light. After he finished the full roll of film and began to rewind the camera to reload, she held up her hand.

"That will have to do," she said. "I've reached my limit. These old shoes are biting my feet."

"Bonnie, thank you so much. I'll take the roll by the express film development, and they'll be ready in time for the article."

"Article?"

"I meet with my editor tomorrow. I've written the first article," he said. "Do you want to read it?"

"Summarize it for me," she said. Royce wondered why she didn't seem excited by this news. Maybe just nervous about the notoriety, he thought.

"I decided it will work best as a series of articles, and I'm telling the story chronologically, just like how it all unfolded between you and me, starting at the cemetery where I first met you," he said. "Eventually, I think this will be a great book, and writing it this way sets up—"

"What can you prove?" she interrupted.

"I told you about that when we met last time. I can prove the funeral was a fake," Royce said. "Or at least cast serious doubt on it. That's real news."

"But we don't know who Sal was or who was killed in our place," she said.

"If we can get enough people to believe your funeral was faked, we can get the court to order an exhumation of the body," he said. "Clyde too."

"Do you remember your promise to me when we met?"

"Um, maybe?"

"You promised you wouldn't publish anything until I could tell you the whole story. We got a long way to go on that story, Royce. A lot more happened," she said. "I got a debt to Clyde to tell the whole thing, and I'm not backing down on that."

Royce thought back to that improbable meeting at the other cemetery when Bonnie had thrown the guns into Clyde's grave. He silently cursed himself for making any kind of promise. He wondered if in some cases, like this one, promises weren't meant to be broken.

"But why wait?" he asked.

"Finding out that our deaths were faked is important, but the big story is who were we working for."

"If we go to print now, people will come out of the woodwork to corroborate it, and at your age..." He let his voice trail off, regretting it already.

"You think I might die?" she said.

"It's possible," he said.

"I do miss Clyde," she said. "Life doesn't seem worth living without him." Her voice was flat, without emotion, a simple statement of fact, and he felt bad for her.

"I'm sorry," Royce said. "I didn't mean to sound unfeeling."

"I know you're excited about this, and for good reason. I promise not to die until I finish. But I can't promise someone won't decide to put me in the grave if we parcel it out."

"Wait, you think you're in danger?" The thought had never occurred to him. "Am I in danger?"

"Clyde and I have been quiet for decades," she said. "After he got shot up so bad he couldn't walk anymore, we were forgotten. But the fact that we worked for such a powerful, secretive group—I don't know where this all leads."

Royce looked around the cemetery, suddenly feeling vulnerable. For the first time since he'd stumbled into this strange story, he wondered about his own safety.

"Bonnie, I like to consider myself a man of honor, but I'm going forward with showing my editor the article," he said. "We'll be safer with the information out."

Bonnie walked back over to the headstone and picked up her coat. Holding it up, she dusted off the grass and dirt from the cloth and then slipped it on. She walked back over to where Royce was standing, stopping very close to him—too close. He could smell the cigar leaf on her breath.

Bonnie looked up at him, her eyes steely. Royce was amazed that this tiny old woman who stood a full foot shorter than him actually seemed to be trying to intimidate him. But then he remembered her history.

"Are you going to shoot me?"

He wondered if he should be physically restraining her.

"No," she said with a laugh. "Just funning with you. But I will deny it all."

"What?" Royce exclaimed. "You can't do that."

"I can, and I will."

"I've got it all on tape."

"If I tell the world that I was playing a game with you and get a doctor to say I got the dementia, what do you think would happen then?" Bonnie asked, without smiling.

Royce realized he had deeply underestimated this

woman. How could he have been so stupid? If she really was Bonnie Parker, she was some kind of genius having survived all these years. Mistaking her for some frail, feeble old woman had blinded him to that.

"Bonnie, Miss Parker, Mrs. Prentiss, any damn one of you, I'll lose my job. I'll be a laughing stock. You can't do that to me," he said.

"Then just wait," she said. "Honor your word. And be patient. Digging up them bodies will tip our hand. We have to find out who Sal worked for first and who died in the car that day instead of us. I promise you, Royce, it will be well worth your while."

She stepped back, and Royce let out a breath he had not realized he was holding. With the exhale, he watched his dreams of his editor toasting him at the Pulitzer award ceremony wilt into the dry Texas air. Okay, he thought. This was the story of a lifetime for someone like him. What were a few more weeks?

He would play by her rules for now.

"Fine, let's get some coffee and maybe a hamburger. I need more information on this Sal person," Royce said.

She looked up at the cloudless blue Texas sky. A lone raven flew silently in the distance.

"Say," she said. "In all your research, did you ever come across anything about the Parker Barrow Benevolence Fund?"

"Yeah, it's some kind of urban legend," Royce said. "Why?"

"Just curious," Bonnie said, tossing her pistol on the seat. "Let's skip the coffee. How about some gin and a pimento cheese sandwich?"

The End

AFTERWORD

After 1934, the Roosevelt administration passed legislation associated with what's commonly called the "second" New Deal. These new laws provided some protections for working Americans as a bulwark against the drive to maximize profits inherent in capitalism.

Among other outcomes, the laws promoted labor unions to provide workers with a collective negotiating voice, defined thresholds for minimum wages and maximum hours, established protections for farm workers, and established Social Security accounts for retired workers—a shared financial responsibility of employers and employees.

Conceptually, the goals implicit in the New Deal proved to be a model for future efforts at balancing the roles of the government and capitalism in ways that maximize opportunities for all Americans in their "pursuit of happiness." An example of a subsequent effort was the 1965 establishment of guaranteed government-backed health care for retired workers through what came to be known as Medicare.

While not without critics and flaws, for more than a half-century, these policies have been intended to ensure that some benefits of capitalism are consistently distributed to the workers that create the goods and services that generate profit, rather than concentrating profit in the hands of the few who own or otherwise control capital.

ABOUT THE AUTHORS

Clark Hays was raised on a ranch in Montana and spent his formative years branding cows, riding horses, and writing. His poetry, creative fiction, and nonfiction have appeared in many journals, magazines, and newspapers. Previously, he was nominated for a Pushcart Prize for a short story appearing in Opium Magazine.

Kathleen McFall was born and raised in Washington, DC. During more than a decade working in journalism, she published hundreds of articles about natural resources, environmental issues, energy, and biomedical science. Previously, she was a director of communications and senior advisor at a major research university. Kathleen was awarded a fellowship for fiction writing from Oregon Literary Arts.

In addition to the *Bonnie and Clyde* books, Clark and Kathleen are the authors of the award-winning, best-selling *The Cowboy and the Vampire Collection*, which was named to *Kirkus Reviews* best books of 2014 list and included in IndieReader's best books of 2016.

The authors live in Portland, Oregon.

Connect with the authors:

www.pumpjackpress.com
www.facebook.com/cowboyandvampire
@cowboyvamp (Twitter)
@cowboyvampire (Instagram)